FIRST-YEAR TECHNICIAN MATHEMATICS

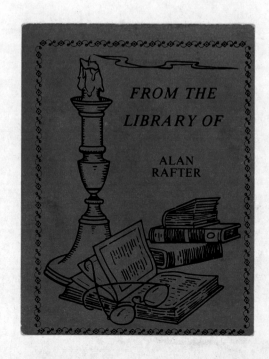

FIRST-YEAR TECHNICIAN MATHEMATICS

for Electrical, Electronics and Telecommunications Students

RHYS LEWIS

B.Sc. Tech., C.Eng., M.I.E.E.
Senior Lecturer, Openshaw Technical College, Manchester

First published 1974 by
THE MACMILLAN PRESS LTD
London and Basingstoke
Associated companies in New York Dublin
Melbourne Johannesburg and Madras

SBN 333 17411 9

Type-setting by The Whitefriars Press Ltd
Printed in Great Britain by litho by The Anchor Press Ltd
and bound by Wm Brendon & Son Ltd
both of Tiptree. Essex

Contents

Contents

Preface

This book is the first in a series of three covering the mathematics syllabuses of courses leading to Electrical and Electronic Technician and ultimately Technician Engineer status. At the present time these courses include the City & Guilds of London Institute courses 280, 281, 285, 270 and 272 and the titles of the books breaking the syllabuses into four years (the third-year text to include mathematical applications) stem from the organisation of these courses. With the advent of the Technician Education Council and subsequent reorganisation of courses it may be found that the breakdown by year will change. However it is anticipated that the total content of all three books will more than adequately cover the total syllabus content of all electrical and electronic technician courses both present and proposed. All three books contain a large number of examples both worked and otherwise and finish with a number of typical examination papers covering the content of each volume.

The assistance and advice of Mr Noel Morris, the series editor, is gratefully acknowledged. In addition the author would particularly like to thank Mrs L.J.E. Jones for typing the manuscript.

Openshaw, Manchester
July 1974

RHYS LEWIS

1 Arithmetic

There are four basic operations. These are addition, subtraction, multiplication and division indicated by the symbols $+$, $-$, $\times$ and $\div$ respectively. Sometimes the multiplication sign is omitted or replaced by the word 'of' and the division sign may be replaced by a line as in $\frac{3}{4}$ (3 divided by 4) or a solidus (¾). It is assumed that the reader is familiar with these basic operations.

Order of operation

When only one operation is indicated, for example, $7 - 4$ or $8 + 5$ the problem of order of operation does not exist. However in an expression containing a number of operations an order of operation is essential. Without one the expression

$$12 - 6 \div 3$$

for example, could equal 2 (taking the subtraction operation before the division) or 10 (taking the division operation first). In fact, in this case, 10 is the correct answer since it is normal practice to perform division *before* subtraction. The order of the four operations is as follows

'of' before division
division before multiplication
multiplication before addition
addition before subtraction

If any part of the expression is bracketed this part must be calculated first regardless of the operations required inside the bracket. The complete rule then is in order of performance

1

brackets before 'of' before division before multiplication before addition before subtraction

By taking the initial letters of each operation we can make the word BODMAS which is an easy method for remembering the order in which operations should be carried out. Such a word used to jog the memory is called a mnemonic — there are a number of such mnemonics in mathematics.

Example 1.1

15 + 5 − 3 equals 17   (addition first)

Example 1.2

9 ÷ 3 − 1 equals 2   (division first)

Example 1.3

25 + 10 − 12 ÷ 4 equals 32   (division first, then addition)

Example 1.4

7 × 3 + 6 equals 27   (multiplication first)

Example 1.5

24 − 3 × 7 equals 3   (multiplication first)

Example 1.6

12 ÷ 3 + 18 ÷ 2 × 3 equals 31   (division first, then multiplication then addition)

Example 1.7

(12 + 8) ÷ (4 − 2) equals 10   (brackets first, then division)

Example 1.6 in more detail is as follows
$$12 \div 3 + 18 \div 2 \times 3$$
Taking division first, this gives
$$4 + 9 \times 3$$
then multiplication which gives
$$4 + 27$$
and finally addition, giving
$$31$$

Note that in example 1.7 the contents of the brackets are first evaluated to give 20 ÷ 2 which equals 10.

The 'of' operation is not demonstrated above since this usually occurs with numbers less than one, that is fractions. These are dealt with later.

Exercise 1.1

Evaluate the following. (An omitted sign between a number and a bracket implies multiplication.)

(1) $12 \div 3 + 15 \div 5$

(2) $12 \div 6 \times 7 - 12$

(3) $12 \times 7 + 4 \times 8$

(4) $12 + 7 (3 + 6)$

(5) $(8 \times 9) \div (6 \times 6)$

(6) $8(9 \times 4 + 3)$

(7) $42 \div 7 \times 6 (3 + 2)$

(8) $15 (8 + 3 \times 2) \div 7$

The equality symbol

So far in this chapter the word *equals* has been written in full. The symbol for equals is = and is included *only* between expressions that are equal. This point may seem obvious; however, very often when making calculations or later on when simplifying expressions containing an equals sign — equations — the mind 'runs on' before the pen and the equality sign is included where it should not be. This point is emphasised again in chapter 4. For the moment the reader is advised to stop and check every time the equals sign is written down.

FRACTIONS

The word fraction means 'a part of' and in arithmetic the term usually means a part of one unit. For example if one unit is divided into three equal parts each part will be of value 1 divided by 3, written as $\frac{1}{3}$ or 1/3 and called 'one-third'; similarly 1 divided by 4 is written $\frac{1}{4}$ or 1/4 and is called 'one-fourth' or 'one-quarter'. When written in this way the number above the line (or to the left of the solidus) is called the *numerator* and the number below the line (or to the right of the solidus) is called the *denominator*. If the numerator is smaller than the denominator, for example 1/3, 5/6, 8/9, etc. then the value of the whole is less than 1 and the term is called a *proper fraction*.

Of course, any number greater than 1 can be written with a numerator and denominator, for example 8/4, 10/5 and 11/5. In these cases we are writing the number in fractional form, that is showing it as being made up of a number of fractions. For example 8/4 which is of course 2, is being written here as 8 parts each of which is one fourth part (one-quarter) of 1. Since four fourth parts (four-quarters) equal one whole one, then eight fourth parts (eight-quarters) must equal two whole ones. The number 2 is a whole number and is, of course, greater than 1. A number written in fractional form which has a value greater than 1 is called an *improper fraction*. Note that whole numbers, for example 2, 3, 4, etc. are called *integers*.

Improper fractions are not necessarily whole numbers. For example 11/5, which was used earlier, is equal to two whole ones plus one-fifth of a whole one. This could be written as $2\frac{1}{5}$ which consists of a whole number 2 and a proper fraction 1/5. When performing calculations on fractions it is usually advisable to avoid the use of mixed numbers such as $2\frac{1}{5}$ and it is far wiser to convert to improper fractions, for example 11/5.

Simplification of fractions

Most integers are the product of two or more other integers. Thus for example we have $6 = 2 \times 3$, $12 = 4 \times 3$ or $2 \times 2 \times 3$, $15 = 5 \times 3$, $28 = 7 \times 4$ or $7 \times 2 \times 2$, and so on. These other integers are called *factors,* so that the number 6 has factors 2 and 3, 12 has factors 4 and 3 or 2, 2 and 3. There are some numbers which do not have factors other than themselves and 1; for example the number 19 can be said to equal 19×1 but other than these it has no factors. Such numbers are called *prime numbers.* Other examples include 1, 3, 5, 7, 11, 13, 17, and so on.

Breaking a number into its factors — the process is called *factorisation* — can be used to simplify fractions. This is because provided that both numerator and denominator of any fraction are divided (or multiplied) by the same number the value of the fraction remains unchanged.

This is clearly seen by examining for example the improper fraction 4/2. This means 4 divided by 2 and is equal to 2. The fraction 4/2 actually means four-halves. Now if both numerator and denominator are multiplied by 2 we have 8/4 which has the value 2 as before. Similarly instead of 4/2 we can write

16/8 (numerator and denominator of 4/2 multiplied by 4)
12/6 (numerator and denominator of 4/2 multiplied by 3)
20/10 (numerator and denominator of 4/2 multiplied by 5)

This process is increasing the size of numerator and denominator and is the opposite of simplification. However, if we begin with the larger numbers 20/10, 12/6, 16/8, etc. and *divide* numerator and denominator by 5, 3 and 4 respectively these fractions simplify to 4/2. Dividing 4/2 by 2 in both numerator and denominator gives 2/1, that is 2 divided by 1 which is of course 2.

The fraction taken above as an example is an improper fraction, that is a number greater than unity being expressed in fractional terms. However, the foregoing comments apply equally to proper fractions, that is those with a value less than 1. Thus 8/16, 4/8, 2/4, when divided throughout by 8, 4 and 2 respectively all equal 1/2.

Example 1.8
Simplify $\dfrac{66}{88}$

$$\frac{66}{88} = \frac{3 \times 2 \times 11}{4 \times 2 \times 11}$$

$$= \frac{3}{4} \qquad \text{(Dividing through by 11 and 2)}$$

Example 1.9

Simplify $\dfrac{108}{810}$

$$\frac{108}{810} = \frac{9 \times 3 \times 2 \times 2}{9 \times 9 \times 5 \times 2}$$

$$= \frac{3 \times 2}{9 \times 5} \text{ (Dividing through by 9 and 2)}$$

$$= \frac{2}{15} \text{ (Dividing through by 3)}$$

Example 1.10

Simplify $\dfrac{180}{360}$

$$\frac{180}{360} = \frac{5 \times 36}{10 \times 36}$$

$$= \frac{1}{2} \text{ (Dividing through by 36 and 5)}$$

Example 1.11

Simplify $\dfrac{169}{845}$

$$\frac{169}{845} = \frac{13 \times 13 \times 1}{13 \times 13 \times 5}$$

$$= \frac{1}{5} \text{ (Dividing through by 13 and 13)}$$

CALCULATIONS WITH FRACTIONS

Multiplication

Multiplication is by far the easiest operation to carry out with fractions. When two fractions are multiplied together their numerators are multiplied to give the resultant numerator and their denominators are multiplied to give the resultant denominator. For example

$$\frac{2}{3} \times \frac{3}{4} = \frac{2 \times 3}{3 \times 4}$$

$$= \frac{6}{12}$$

which is the resultant fraction. This answer may be simplified since the denominator 12 has factors 6 x 2 and 6 may be divided into both numerator and denominator as follows

$$\frac{6}{12} = \frac{6 \times 1}{6 \times 2}$$

$$= \frac{1}{2}$$

Thus

$$\frac{2}{3} \times \frac{3}{4} = \frac{1}{2}$$

As stated earlier the multiplication operation particularly with fractions is often indicated by the word 'of'. An example of this follows.

Find the length of 2/3 of a piece of wood 4 metres in length.

The length required is 2/3 of 4 metres, that is

$$\frac{2}{3} \times 4$$

Multiplying numerators yields 8, multiplying denominators yields 3 (3 x 1 since 4 may be regarded as 4/1). Thus

$$\frac{2}{3} \times 4 = \frac{8}{3}$$

This is an improper fraction and may be expressed as a mixed number, that is a whole number and a proper fraction, as follows

$$\frac{8}{3} = 2\tfrac{2}{3}$$

Thus 2/3 of 4 metres is $2\tfrac{2}{3}$ metres (two and two-thirds metres).

Example 1.12

$$\frac{3}{4} \times \frac{2}{5}$$

$$= \frac{3 \times 2}{4 \times 5} = \frac{3}{2 \times 5} \quad \text{(dividing through by 2)}$$

$$= \frac{3}{10}$$

Example 1.13

$$\frac{13}{14} \times \frac{5}{7} \times 2$$

$$= \frac{13 \times 5}{7 \times 7} \quad \text{(dividing through by 2)}$$

$$= \frac{65}{49}$$

This cannot be simplified further since 65 and 49 do not share common factors.

Example 1.14

$$\frac{3}{5} \text{ of } \frac{6}{7}$$

$$= \frac{3 \times 6}{5 \times 7}$$

$$= \frac{18}{35}$$

This cannot be simplified further.

Example 1.15

$$\frac{14}{15} \text{ of } 60$$

$$= \frac{14}{15} \times 60$$

$$= 14 \times 4 \text{ (dividing 60 by 15)}$$

$$= 56$$

Division

As with multiplication, when a fraction is divided by another fraction, the numerator of the fraction being divided is divided by the numerator of the dividing fraction and similarly with the denominators.

For example $6/8 \div 3/2$. The numerator of the answer is $6/3$, that is 2; the denominator of the answer is $8/2$, that is 4; and the answer is $2/4$ which simplifies to $1/2$.

A simple rule for division is to change the division sign to a multiplication and turn the dividing fraction upside down. This gives the correct answer in all cases.

Thus

$$\frac{6}{8} \div \frac{3}{2} = \frac{6}{8} \times \frac{2}{3}$$

$$= \frac{2}{4}$$

$$= \frac{1}{2} \text{ as before}$$

Example 1.16

$$\frac{13}{15} \div \frac{26}{45}$$

$$= \frac{13}{15} \times \frac{45}{26}$$

$$= \frac{3}{2} \text{ (Dividing through by 13 and 15)}$$

Example 1.17

$$\frac{7}{9} \times \frac{4}{11} \div \frac{56}{198}$$

$$= \frac{28}{99} \times \frac{198}{56}$$

$$= \frac{2}{2} \text{ (Dividing through by 28 and 99)}$$

$$= 1$$

Example 1.18

$$\frac{2}{3} \text{ of } \frac{21}{15} \div \frac{7}{5}$$

$$= \frac{2}{3} \times \frac{21}{15} \times \frac{5}{7}$$

$$= \frac{2}{3} \text{ (Dividing through by 7, 3 and 5)}$$

Exercise 1.2

Simplify and leave in fractional form

(a) $\dfrac{13}{15} \times \dfrac{2}{3}$

(b) $\dfrac{3}{7}$ of $\dfrac{21}{126}$

(c) $\dfrac{2}{3} \left(\dfrac{3}{5} \text{ of } \dfrac{7}{9} \right)$

(d) $\dfrac{5}{7}$ of $\dfrac{8}{15} \times \dfrac{3}{4}$

(e) $\dfrac{12}{13} \div \dfrac{36}{26}$

(f) $\dfrac{4}{5}$ of $\dfrac{8}{9} \div \dfrac{4}{3}$

(g) $\dfrac{9}{21} \left(\dfrac{3}{5} \text{ of } \dfrac{11}{17} \div \dfrac{4}{34} \right)$

(h) $\dfrac{7}{8} \left(\dfrac{5}{16} \text{ of } \dfrac{8}{9} \text{ of } \dfrac{4}{3} \right) \div \dfrac{6}{7}$

Addition and Subtraction

In addition of fractions the final answer is *not* given by the sum of numerators divided by the sum of denominators. Numerators can only be added if the denominator of all the fractions concerned is the same.

This is easily seen from the following. Consider

$$\frac{2}{3} + \frac{2}{3}$$

Adding numerators gives 4, adding denominators gives 6, so we have 4/6 which equals 2/3 (dividing through by 2). Clearly 2/3 + 2/3 cannot equal 2/3. This would be equivalent to saying that 1 plus 1 equals 1.

Now 2/3 means two-thirds, so that two-thirds plus two-thirds equals four-thirds — the numerators are added provided that the denominators are the same. Since all denominators may not be the same it is necessary to change some or all of the fractions so that the denominator of each one is the same throughout. One way of finding a suitable common-denominator is to multiply the denominators and then modify the numerators accordingly.

For example, simplify

$$\frac{1}{15} + \frac{1}{10}$$

A common denominator is 15 × 10 giving 150. First change 1/15 to have 150 as denominator. Remember that whatever is done to the denominator in the way of multiplication or division must be done to the numerator otherwise the value of the fraction will change. To write 1/15 (one-fifteenth) in terms of a denominator of 150 it is necessary to multiply 15 by 10. Thus the numerator must also be multiplied by the same number, that is

$$\frac{1}{15} = \frac{10}{150}$$

Similarly

$$\frac{1}{10} = \frac{15}{150} \text{ (multiplying through by 15)}$$

and so

$$\frac{1}{15} + \frac{1}{10} = \frac{10}{150} + \frac{15}{150}$$

$$= \frac{10 + 15}{150}$$

$$= \frac{25}{150}$$

$$= \frac{1}{6} \text{ (dividing through by 25)}$$

In the preceding example 150 was taken as the common denominator. Simplification took place on the last line. To avoid using numbers larger than necessary and thus to begin simplification as early as possible in the calculation it is advisable to find the *lowest* common denominator in the first instance. This is obtained by finding the *lowest common multiple* (L.C.M.) of all the denominators, that is the lowest number of which each denominator is a factor. In the above example 150 was taken as the common denominator but this not the lowest (and therefore not the simplest) common denominator. What is required is the lowest common multiple of 10 and 15, that is the lowest number of which both 10 and 15 are factors. This is in fact 30. It is found as follows

the factors of 10 are 5 × 2
the factors of 15 are 5 × 3

The lowest common multiple is obtained by multiplying together all the factors *without unnecessary duplication*. Thus

$$5 \times 2 \times 3 \quad \text{(5 appears only once)}$$

so the lowest common denominator is 30 and the above example becomes

$$\frac{1}{10} + \frac{1}{15} = \frac{3}{30} + \frac{2}{30}$$

$$= \frac{5}{30}$$

$$= \frac{1}{6}$$

Simplification still takes place on the last line but the numerators (3 and 2) are smaller than in the previous case (10 and 15). Finding the lowest common denominator becomes increasingly advantageous as the denominators of the various fractions become larger.

Consider for example

$$\frac{11}{18} + \frac{23}{27}$$

A common denominator is 18 × 27 but this number is unnecessarily large. The factors of 18 are 2 × 9 and of 27 are 3 × 9. The L.C.M. is 2 × 9 × 3, that is 54 and the problem becomes

$$\frac{33}{54} + \frac{46}{54} = \frac{79}{54}$$

which cannot be further simplified.

Note that 11/18 becomes 33/54 by multiplying through by 3 and that 23/27 becomes 46/54 by multiplying through by 2.

Example 1.19

Find the L.C.M. of 21, 9, 6.

Factors of 21 are 7 × 3, factors of 9 are 3 × 3 and factors of 6 are 3 × 2.
Now 7 × 3 × 2, which is the multiple of the factors without any duplication,

gives 42. This is not the L.C.M. since 9 is not a factor of 42. We must therefore take another of the unused factors. There are four 3s and only one has been used. So we now try $7 \times 3 \times 2 \times 3$ giving 126. 9 is a factor of 126 and so are 21 and 6. Thus 126 is the L.C.M. and could be taken as the lowest common denominator if 21, 9 and 6 were denominators in a calculation involving fractions.

Example 1.20

Find the L.C.M. of 5, 12 and 14.

Factors of 5 are 5×1 (5 is a prime number), factors of 12 are $2 \times 2 \times 3$ and of 14 are 7×2.

First try $5 \times 2 \times 3 \times 7$ (each factor included only once). This gives 210 which does not have 12 as a factor.

Now try $5 \times 2 \times 3 \times 7 \times 2$ (using 2 again) giving 420 of which 12, 14 and 5 are factors. Thus the L.C.M. is 420.

Example 1.21

Find the L.C.M. of 3, 9, 21 and 24.

The factors of 3 are 3×1 (prime number), of 9 are 3×3, of 21 are 7×3 and of 24 are $2 \times 2 \times 2 \times 3$.

First try $2 \times 3 \times 7$ (each factor once). This equals 42 and only 3 and 21 are factors.

Next try $2 \times 3 \times 7 \times 2$ (using 2 twice). This equals 84 and again only 3 and 21 are factors.

Next try $2 \times 3 \times 7 \times 2 \times 2$ (using 2 three times).
This equals 168 and is the L.C.M.

From the above examples the procedure is fairly clear.

(1)   Break each number into its lowest possible factors;
(2)   find the multiple of all factors, each one used once;
(3)   if not suitable multiply the number so far obtained by the remaining unused factors, one at a time in order of magnitude, bearing in mind that the idea is to increase the multiple in as small stages as possible, until the lowest integral multiple of all the original numbers is obtained.

When subtracting one fraction from another the procedure is similar to that of addition except of course that in this instance subtraction of numerators takes place once the lowest common denominator has been found.

Example 1.22

Simplify $\dfrac{4}{5} - \dfrac{1}{3}$

$$\frac{4}{5} - \frac{1}{3} = \frac{12 - 5}{15}$$

$$= \frac{7}{15}$$

Example 1.23

Simplify $\frac{12}{13} - \frac{4}{9}$

$$\frac{12}{13} - \frac{4}{9} = \frac{108 - 52}{117}$$

$$= \frac{56}{117}$$

which cannot be further simplified.

Example 1.24

Simplify $\frac{15}{16} - \frac{3}{8} - \frac{1}{2}$

$$= \frac{15 - 6 - 8}{16}$$

$$= \frac{15 - 14}{16}$$

$$= \frac{1}{16}$$

Notice that here $-6 - 8 = -(6 + 8)$ that is -14. Manipulation of signs is considered in detail in chapter 3.

A mixed set of examples follows. The reader should follow the working in each case with great care and ensure that an understanding of the principles involved is obtained by re-reading the relevant sections where necessary.

Example 1.25

Simplify $\frac{2}{3}$ of $\left(\frac{4}{5} + \frac{1}{4} \right)$

$$\frac{2}{3} \text{ of } \left(\frac{4}{5} + \frac{1}{4} \right) = \frac{2}{3} \times \left(\frac{4}{5} + \frac{1}{4} \right)$$

$$= \frac{2}{3} \times \left(\frac{16 + 5}{20} \right)$$

$$= \frac{2}{3} \times \frac{21}{20}$$

$$= \frac{7}{10}$$

Example 1.26

Simplify $\frac{1}{5}$ of $\left(\frac{8}{9} - \frac{1}{3}\right) \div \frac{2}{5}$

$$\frac{1}{5} \text{ of } \left(\frac{8}{9} - \frac{1}{3}\right) \div \frac{2}{5} = \frac{1}{5} \times \left(\frac{8-3}{9}\right) \div \frac{2}{5}$$

$$= \frac{1}{5} \times \frac{5}{9} \div \frac{2}{5}$$

$$= \frac{1}{5} \times \frac{5}{9} \times \frac{5}{2}$$

$$= \frac{5}{18}$$

Example 1.27

Simplify $\left(\frac{13}{20} + \frac{4}{5}\right) \div \left(\frac{11}{18} - \frac{2}{5}\right)$

$$\left(\frac{13}{20} + \frac{4}{5}\right) \div \left(\frac{11}{18} - \frac{2}{5}\right) = \left(\frac{13+16}{20}\right) \div \left(\frac{55-36}{90}\right)$$

$$= \frac{29}{20} \div \frac{19}{90}$$

$$= \frac{29}{20} \times \frac{90}{19}$$

$$= \frac{261}{38}$$

$$= 6\frac{33}{38}$$

Example 1.28

Simplify $\frac{1}{3}$ of $(4\frac{2}{5} + 3\frac{7}{8}) \div (3\frac{1}{7} - 2\frac{1}{2})$

This example involves mixed numbers. It is advisable to convert these to improper fractions before commencing.

$$\frac{1}{3} \text{ of } (4\tfrac{2}{5} + 3\tfrac{7}{8}) \div (3\tfrac{1}{7} - 2\tfrac{1}{2}) = \frac{1}{3} \times \left(\frac{22}{5} + \frac{31}{8}\right) \div \left(\frac{22}{7} - \frac{5}{2}\right)$$

$$= \frac{1}{3} \left(\frac{176+155}{40}\right) \div \left(\frac{44-35}{14}\right)$$

$$= \frac{1}{3} \times \frac{331}{40} \div \frac{9}{14}$$

$$= \frac{1}{3} \times \frac{331}{40} \times \frac{14}{9}$$

$$= \frac{331 \times 7}{27 \times 20} = \frac{2317}{540}$$

$$= 4\tfrac{157}{540}$$

Note in the above example the conversion to improper fractions

$$4\tfrac{2}{5} = \frac{4 \times 5 + 2}{5} \text{ that is } \frac{22}{5}$$

$$3\tfrac{7}{8} = \frac{3 \times 8 + 7}{8} \text{ that is } \frac{31}{8}$$

$$3\tfrac{1}{7} = \frac{3 \times 7 + 1}{7} \text{ that is } \frac{22}{7}$$

$$2\tfrac{1}{2} = \frac{2 \times 2 + 1}{2} \text{ that is } \frac{5}{2}$$

The idea of this is to convert the whole number to fractional form by multiplying the whole number by the proper-fraction denominator and adding this to the proper-fraction numerator to give the improper-fraction numerator. The improper-fraction denominator is of course the same as the proper-fraction denominator.

Example 1.29

Simplify $(4\tfrac{1}{3} \times 3\tfrac{1}{5}) + (2\tfrac{7}{8} \times 1\tfrac{1}{8}) - (3\tfrac{1}{5} - 2\tfrac{1}{10})$

Converting to improper fractions this expression may be written

$$\left(\frac{13}{3} \times \frac{16}{5}\right) + \left(\frac{23}{8} \times \frac{9}{8}\right) - \left(\frac{16}{5} - \frac{21}{10}\right)$$

$$= \frac{208}{15} + \frac{207}{64} - \left(\frac{32 - 21}{10}\right)$$

$$= \frac{208}{15} + \frac{207}{64} - \frac{11}{10}$$

The factors of 15 are 5×3, of 64 are $2 \times 2 \times 2 \times 2 \times 2 \times 2$ and of 10 are 5×2.

$5 \times 3 \times 2$ is not suitable for a common denominator and by continuing the process as described earlier $5 \times 3 \times 2 \times 2 \times 2 \times 2 \times 2 \times 2$ is the lowest common denominator. This equals 960. Thus

$$\frac{208}{15} + \frac{207}{64} - \frac{11}{10} = \frac{208 \times 64}{960} + \frac{207 \times 15}{960} - \frac{11 \times 96}{960}$$

$$= \frac{13\,312 + 3105 - 1056}{960}$$

$$= \frac{15\,361}{960} \text{ or } 16\tfrac{1}{960}$$

It will be seen that the figures in the last example are cumbersome. On occasions like this it is advisable to use decimal fractions to be described later.

Exercise 1.3

Simplify the following leaving the answer in fractional form (proper or otherwise)

(a) $\frac{7}{8} + \frac{5}{16} + \frac{3}{4} - \frac{1}{2} - \frac{1}{32}$

(b) $\frac{15}{19} - \frac{1}{2} + \frac{13}{19}$

(c) $4\frac{3}{8} + 5\frac{1}{4} - 7\frac{1}{16}$

(d) $8\frac{1}{9} - 6\frac{2}{3} - 1\frac{1}{27}$

(e) $\frac{2}{3}$ of $(4\frac{1}{3} + 3\frac{1}{8})$

(f) $\frac{4}{5} \div \frac{1}{3}$ of $(7\frac{1}{8} + 4\frac{7}{8})$

(g) $(3\frac{1}{3} \div 4\frac{1}{2}) + \frac{1}{2}$ of $6\frac{3}{4}$

(h) $\frac{1}{4}$ of $15\frac{1}{2} \div \frac{1}{3}$ of $7\frac{1}{8}$

(i) $\frac{7}{9}$ of $(4\frac{1}{3} + 5\frac{6}{9}) \div 3\frac{1}{2}$

(j) $7\frac{1}{8} \times (3\frac{1}{4} + 4\frac{1}{2}) \div \frac{1}{2}$ of $\frac{31}{4}$

OTHER ARITHMETICAL PROCESSES – RAISING TO A POWER

When a number is multiplied by itself once or more than once the process is called *raising to a power*. For example

3 raised to the power 2 is 3 × 3
3 raised to the power 3 is 3 × 3 × 3
3 raised to the power 4 is 3 × 3 × 3 × 3

Notice that the number being raised to the power appears a number of times equal to the power (twice when raising to the power 2, three times when raising to the power 3).

Notice also that the number being raised to a power is multiplied *by itself* a number of times equal to one *less* than the power; that is in the above example 3 is multiplied *once* by 3 when raising to the power *two* and *twice* by 3 when raising to the power *three*.

The notation used for the process of raising to a power is that of writing the power above the number being raised as follows

3 raised to the power 2 is written 3^2
3 raised to the power 3 is written 3^3

Note that raising to the power 2 is also called 'squaring' so that 3^2 is '3 squared' that is 3 × 3 = 9. Similarly 3 raised to the power 3, that is 3^3, is called '3 cubed'. Special names are not normally used for other powers.

Provided that the number being raised, often called the *base*, is the same in an expression containing a number of such terms, powers may be added or subtracted depending on whether the terms are being multiplied or divided. Thus

$$4^3 \times 4^2 = (4 \times 4 \times 4) \times (4 \times 4)$$
$$= 4^{3+2} = 4^5$$

and we see that the power 3 has been *added* to the power 2 to give the final resultant power. Note however that the base (in this case, 4) *must* be the *same* throughout the expression. Similarly

$$3^2 \times 3^3 \times 3 = (3 \times 3) \times (3 \times 3 \times 3) \times 3$$
$$= 3^{2+3+1} = 3^6$$

This example shows that any number on its own may be considered to be that number raised to the power 1.

  RULE *In an expression containing a number of terms multiplied together, each term consisting of a base raised to a power, the powers may be ADDED together to give the resultant power. Each term must contain the same base.*

Example 1.30
$$4^2 \times 4^3 = 4^5$$

Example 1.31
$$5^3 \times 5^2 \times 5 = 5^6$$

Example 1.32
$$3^2 \times 3 \times 3^4 = 3^7$$

Example 1.33
$$2^3 \times 2^2 + 3^4 \times 3^2 = 2^5 + 3^6$$

Example 1.34
$$4^2 \times 4 + 2^3 \times 2 = 4^3 + 2^4$$

Example 1.35
$$3(3^3 \times 3 + 4^2 \times 4) = 3(3^4 + 4^3)$$

Example 1.36
$$3(4^2 \times 4^3) - 2(3^2 \times 3) = 3(4^5) - 2(3^3)$$

The above examples may be evaluated completely as follows
1.30
$$4^5 = 4 \times 4 \times 4 \times 4 \times 4$$
$$= 1024$$

1.31
$$5^6 = 5 \times 5 \times 5 \times 5 \times 5 \times 5$$
$$= 15\ 625$$

1.32
$$3^7 = 3 \times 3 \times 3 \times 3 \times 3 \times 3 \times 3$$
$$= 2187$$

1.33

$$2^5 + 3^6 = (2 \times 2 \times 2 \times 2 \times 2) + (3 \times 3 \times 3 \times 3 \times 3 \times 3)$$
$$= 32 + 729$$
$$= 761$$

1.34

$$4^3 + 2^4 = (4 \times 4 \times 4) + (2 \times 2 \times 2 \times 2)$$
$$= 64 + 16$$
$$= 80$$

1.35

$$3(3^4 + 4^3) = 3(3 \times 3 \times 3 \times 3 + 4 \times 4 \times 4)$$
$$= 3(81 + 64)$$
$$= 3 \times 145$$
$$= 435$$

1.36

$$3(4^5) - 2(3^3) = 3(4 \times 4 \times 4 \times 4 \times 4) - 2(3 \times 3 \times 3)$$
$$= 3 \times 1024 - 2 \times 27$$
$$= 3072 - 54$$
$$= 3018$$

It should be noted that when evaluating it is not necessary to write out multiplication in full. This was done above to re-emphasise the meaning of powers.

When terms containing a base raised to a power are divided by terms containing the same base raised to a power the powers may be subtracted. Thus

$$3^5 \div 3^2 = 3 \times 3 \times 3 \times 3 \times 3 \div 3 \times 3$$
$$= 243 \div 9$$
$$= 27$$

and

$$27 = 3^3 \text{ that is } 3^{5-2}$$

Similarly

$$4^3 \div 4 = 64 \div 4$$
$$= 16$$
$$= 4^2 \text{ that is } 4^{3-1}$$

RULE *In an expression containing a term divided by another term, each term consisting of a base raised to a power, the power to which the base is raised in the dividing term is subtracted from the power to which the base is raised in the term being divided. Each term must contain the same base.*

Example 1.37

$$4^5 \div 4^2 = 4^3$$

Example 1.38
$$3^7 \div 3^2 = 3^5$$

Example 1.39
$$\frac{2^4}{2^2} = 2^2$$

Example 1.40
$$4^3 \times 4^2 \div 4 = 4^3 \times 4 \text{ (division first)}$$
$$= 4^4$$

Example 1.41
$$\frac{5^3 \times 5^2}{5 \times 5} = \frac{5^5}{5^2}$$
$$= 5^3$$

Raising to the power unity and zero

As we have seen, raising a number to a power means multiplying the number by itself a number of times equal to one less than the power. Thus 2^2 means 2 multiplied by itself once, that is 2×2. It follows that 2^1 means 2, that is 2 *not* multiplied by itself at all (since one less than the power is zero).

Raising to the power zero appears totally inexplicable using the basic rules but by looking at the rules of division, that is subtraction of powers, we see that $2^2 \div 2^2$, for example, means 2^{2-2} that is 2^0, and since any number (in this case 2^2 or 4) divided by itself is equal to one then $2^0 = 1$.

In general raising any number to the power zero yields unity. Thus $1^0 = 1$, $2^0 = 1$, $3^0 = 1$, $4^0 = 1$ and so on.

Multiple powers

When a number which consists of a base raised to a power is itself raised to a power the result is equal to the base raised to the *product* of the two powers. For example
$$(2^3)^2 = 2^{3 \times 2} \text{ that is } 2^6$$
This is easily seen as follows
$$(2^3)^2 = 2^3 \times 2^3$$
$$= (2 \times 2 \times 2) \times (2 \times 2 \times 2)$$
$$= 2^6 \text{ that is } 2^{3 \times 2}$$

Example 1.42
$$(4^3)^2 = 4^6$$

Example 1.43

$$(3^2)^3 \div (3^2)^2 = 3^6 \div 3^4$$
$$= 3^2 \text{ that is } 3^{6-4}$$

Example 1.44

$$[(5^3)^2]^2 = 5^{3 \times 2 \times 2}$$
$$= 5^{12}$$

Exercise 1.4

Simplify the following (do not calculate the final answers)

(1) $4^3 \times 4^2 \div 4$

(2) $7^4 \div 7^2 \times 7$

(3) $9^4 \times 9^2 \times 9^3 \div 9 \times 9^2$

(4) $8 \times 8^4 \div 8^2$

(5) $6^3 \times 6^2 \div 6 \times 6$

(6) $\dfrac{7^4 \times 7^3}{7 \times 7^2}$

(7) $\dfrac{3^5 \div 3^2}{3}$

(8) $\dfrac{2^2 \times 2^4}{2} + \dfrac{3^2 \times 3^3}{3^4}$

(9) $\dfrac{2^2 \times 3^4 \times 4^2}{2 \times 3^2 \times 4}$

(10) $\dfrac{4^3 \times 4 \times 5^2 \times 5 \times 3^3}{3 \times 3^2 \times 5^3 \times 4^4}$

(11) $(2^2)^3$

(12) $(3^3)^2 + (3^2)^3$

(13) $4^2 + (4^2)^3 - (4^3)^2$

(14) $[(4^2)^3]^5$

(15) $\dfrac{(2^3)^3}{(2^4)^2}$

Note In parts 9 and 10 be careful to apply the rules only to terms containing the same bases.

Use of factors

Earlier in the chapter we examined the process of factorisation of a number in order to simplify fractions. Factorisation is the process of splitting a number into its factors, that is the numbers which when multiplied together give the number being factorised. Factorisation is often a useful aid in simplifying problems containing powers.

Consider the following example.

Example 1.45

Simplify $4^3 \times 16^2$

Since the base is not the same in each term the rule of addition of powers cannot be applied. However, the factors of 16 are 4×4, that is 4^2. Thus

$$4^3 \times 16^2 = 4^3 \times (4^2)^2$$
$$= 4^3 \times 4^4 \text{ (multiply powers)}$$
$$= 4^7 \qquad \text{(add powers)}$$

Example 1.46

Simplify $2^3 \times 8^2 \times 32 \times 16$

Now

$$8 = 2^3$$
$$32 = 2^5$$
$$16 = 2^4$$

and thus

$$2^3 \times 8^2 \times 32 \times 16 = 2^3 \times (2^3)^2 \times 2^5 \times 2^4$$
$$= 2^3 \times 2^6 \times 2^5 \times 2^4$$
$$= 2^{18}$$

Example 1.47

Simplify $8^3 \times 6^4 \times 9^2$

Since

$$8 = 2^3$$
$$6 = 3 \times 2$$
$$9 = 3 \times 3$$

The expression may be written

$$(2^3)^3 \times (3 \times 2)^4 \times (3 \times 3)^2$$

and since

$$(2^3)^3 = 2^9 \text{ (multiply powers)}$$

and

$$(3 \times 2)^4 = 3^4 \times 2^4$$

note that *all* terms within the bracket are raised to the power indicated outside —
4 in this case.
And

$$(3 \times 3)^2 = 3^2 \times 3^2$$
$$= 3^4$$
$$8^3 \times 6^4 \times 9^2 = 2^9 \times 3^4 \times 2^4 \times 3^4$$
$$= 2^{13} \times 3^8 \text{ (add powers)}$$

This is as far as we can go in the way of simplification.

Example 1.48

Simplify $(3^3)^2 \times (9^2)^3 \times (27)^2$

$$= 3^6 \times 3^{12} \times 3^6$$
$$= 3^{24}$$

The reader is left to satisfy himself as to the correctness of this answer.

Raising fractions to a power

The rules given above for raising whole numbers to a power apply equally to fractions. Care must be taken to ensure that the power is applied equally to both numerator and denominator. For example

$$\left(\frac{2}{5}\right)^2 \text{ means } \frac{2^2}{5^2} \text{ that is } \frac{4}{25}$$

Similarly

$$\left(\frac{4}{9}\right)^3 \text{ means } \frac{4^3}{9^3} \text{ that is } \frac{64}{729}$$

Example 1.49

Simplify $\left(\frac{3}{7}\right)^2 \times \left(\frac{3}{7}\right)$

$$= \left(\frac{3}{7}\right)^{2+1} \text{ (add powers)}$$

that is

$$\frac{3^3}{7^3} = \frac{27}{343}$$

Example 1.50

Simplify $\left(\frac{2}{5}\right)^4 \div \left(\frac{2}{5}\right)^2$

$$= \left(\frac{2}{5}\right)^{4-2}$$

that is

$$\frac{2^2}{5^2} = \frac{4}{25}$$

In the previous two examples the same base was used in the terms being multiplied or divided. As with whole numbers being raised to a power the base *must* be the same for the rules regarding addition or subtraction of powers to apply.

When simplifying expressions containing different bases simplify each base first, it may then be possible to apply the rules of power addition or subtraction to either numerator or denominator or both. This is shown in the following example.

Example 1.51

Simplify $\left(\frac{4}{5}\right)^3 \div \left(\frac{5}{8}\right)^2$

$$= \frac{4^3}{5^3} \div \frac{5^2}{8^2}$$

Changing the division sign to one of multiplication and turning the dividing fraction upside down yields

$$\frac{4^3}{5^3} \times \frac{8^2}{5^2}$$

that is

$$\frac{4^3 \times 8^2}{5^3 \ \ 5^2}$$

$$= \frac{4^3 \times 8^2}{5^5}$$

The expression may be further simplified by expressing 8 as (2×4) and using brackets. Thus

$$8^2 = (2 \times 4)^2 \text{ that is } 2^2 \times 4^2$$

(notice the power outside the bracket applies to *all* terms inside the bracket)

$$= 4 \times 4^2$$

$$= 4^3$$

and replacing 8^2 in the numerator of the above fraction by 4^3 we have

$$\frac{4^3 \times 4^3}{5^5}$$

that is

$$\frac{4^6}{5^5}$$

Thus

$$\left(\frac{4}{5}\right)^3 \div \left(\frac{5}{8}\right)^2 = \frac{4^6}{5^5}$$

Example 1.52

$$\left(\frac{3}{7}\right)^3 \div \left(\frac{7}{9}\right)^4$$

$$= \frac{3^3}{7^3} \times \frac{9^4}{7^4} \text{ (changing the division sign)}$$

$$= \frac{3^3 \times (3 \times 3)^4}{7^3 \times 7^4} \text{ (replacing 9 by 3 \times 3)}$$

$$= \frac{3^3 \times 3^4 \times 3^4}{7^3 \times 7^4}$$

$$= \frac{3^{11}}{7^7}$$

Fractional powers

As previously stated, raising a number to a power means multiplying a number by itself a number of times equal to 1 less than the power, thus 4^3 means $4 \times 4 \times 4$ (4 multiplied twice by 4). The opposite process to raising to a power is the determination of *roots* of a number. For example finding the *second* (or *square*) root of a munber means finding the base which when multiplied by itself *once* (that is squared) equals the number. Finding the *third* (or *cube*) root of a number means finding the base which when multiplied by itself *twice* (that is cubed) equals the number. Finding the *fifth* root of a number means finding the base which when multiplied by itself four times equals the number and so on. Thus

the square root of 9 is 3 since $3 \times 3 = 9$
the cube root of 27 is 3 since $3 \times 3 \times 3 = 27$
the fourth root of 16 is 2 since $2 \times 2 \times 2 \times 2 = 16$
the fifth root of 3125 is 5 since $5 \times 5 \times 5 \times 5 \times 5 = 3125$

The root-finding process is indicated by a fractional power; for example square root by the power of 1/2, third or cube root by the power of 1/3, fourth root by the power of 1/4 and so on. The *surd* symbol may also be used, that is, $\sqrt{}$, for square root, $\sqrt[3]{}$ for cube root and so on.
Thus

$$9^{1/2} = 3 \text{ or } \sqrt{9} = 3$$
$$27^{1/3} = 3 \text{ or } \sqrt[3]{27} = 3$$
$$16^{1/4} = 2 \text{ or } \sqrt[4]{16} = 2$$
$$3125^{1/5} = 5 \text{ or } \sqrt[5]{3125} = 5$$

All the rules that apply to whole-number powers apply equally to fractional powers. Thus if the base is the same, fractional powers may be added or subtracted when the terms containing the base are multiplied or divided.

Example 1.53

$$16^{1/4} \times 16^{1/4} = 16^{1/4+1/4}$$
$$= 16^{1/2}$$

This is clearly seen since $16^{1/4}$ (the fourth root of 16) is 2 and thus

$$16^{1/4} \times 16^{1/4} = 2 \times 2$$
$$= 4$$

Now $16^{1/2}$ means the square root of 16 which is 4
Thus

$$16^{1/4} \times 16^{1/4} = 2 \times 2$$
$$= 4$$
$$= 16^{1/2}$$

Example 1.54

$$16^{1/2} \div 16^{1/4} = 16^{1/2-1/4}$$
$$= 16^{1/4}$$

that is

$$4 \div 2 = 2$$

Now examine a more complex example
$$27^{1/3} \times 27^{1/3} = 27^{1/3+1/3}$$
$$= 27^{2/3}$$

Since
$$\frac{2}{3} = \frac{1}{3} \times 2$$

$27^{2/3}$ may be written
$$27^{1/3 \times 2}$$

that is
$$(27^{1/3})^2$$

from the rule of multiple powers considered earlier. Now $27^{1/3}$ means the third or cube root of 27, that is 3. Thus $(27^{1/3})^2$ means 3^2, that is 9.

This could be looked at another way: instead of writing $27^{2/3}$ as $(27^{1/3})^2$ write it as $(27^2)^{1/3}$ which should yield the same result since
$$(27^2)^{1/3} = 27^{2 \times 1/3} \text{ that is } 27^{2/3}$$

Now
$$27^2 = 729$$

thus $(27^2)^{1/3}$ means the cube root of 729 and since $9 \times 9 \times 9 = 729$ then 9 is the required cube root.

Returning to the example
$$27^{1/3} \times 27^{1/3} = 3 \times 3$$

that is the cube root of 27 multiplied by the cube root of 27 and thus
$$27^{1/3} \times 27^{1/3} = 9$$

which is the same result as that obtained from $27^{2/3}$.

Example 1.55
Simplify $(16^{1/2})^{1/2}$

$$(16^{1/2})^{1/2} = 16^{1/2 \times 1/2}$$
from the rule of multiple powers
$$= 16^{1/4}$$
that is the fourth root of 16
$$= 2$$
since $16 = 2 \times 2 \times 2 \times 2$

Example 1.56
Simplify (without working out the answer)
$$\frac{27^{2/3} \times 16^{1/4} \times 125^{1/3}}{16^{1/8} \times 125^{1/6} \times 27^{1/3}}$$

Applying the rules of powers to those terms having the same base the expression may be written
$$27^{2/3 - 1/3} \times 16^{1/4 - 1/8} \times 125^{1/3 - 1/6}$$

and since

$$\frac{2}{3} - \frac{1}{3} = \frac{1}{3}, \quad \frac{1}{4} - \frac{1}{8} = \frac{1}{8} \text{ and } \frac{1}{3} - \frac{1}{6} = \frac{1}{6}$$

then the expression may be written

$$27^{1/3} \times 16^{1/8} \times 125^{1/6}$$

that is the cube root of 27 × the eighth root of 16 × the sixth root of 125.
This may be simplified further since

$$27 = 3^3, 16 = 2^3 \text{ and } 125 = 5^3$$

giving

$$27^{1/3} \times 16^{1/8} \times 125^{1/6} = (3^3)^{1/3} \times (2^3)^{1/8} \times (5^3)^{1/6}$$
$$= 3 \times 2^{3/8} \times 5^{1/2} \text{ (using multiple powers)}$$

Example 1.57

Simplify $(24^3)^{1/8} \times (24^{1/8})^3$

The expression equals $24^{3/8} \times 24^{3/8}$ (using multiple powers)
$$= 24^{3/8 + 3/8} \text{ (using addition of powers)}$$
$$= 24^{6/8}$$
$$= 24^{3/4} \text{ (by simplifying the fractional power)}$$

that is the fourth root of the cube of 24 (or the cube of the fourth root of 24).

Exercise 1.5

Simplify the following, leaving the answer in the form of a base raised to a power.
(1) $8^4 \times 16^3 \times 32$
(2) $3^2 \times 9^2 \times 27^2$
(3) $5 \times 25 \times 125 \times 5^3$
(4) $2^3 \times 16 \times 8^2 \times 4^4$
(5) $7^8 \div 49^2 \times 343^2$

Simplify the following, leaving the answer in the form of a fraction raised to a power.

(6) $\left(\frac{5}{6}\right)^4 \div \left(\frac{36}{25}\right)^2$

(7) $\left(\frac{4}{9}\right)^3 \times \left(\frac{16}{81}\right)^4$

(8) $\left(\frac{9}{16}\right)^2 \div \left(\frac{256}{81}\right)^3$

Simplify the following and evaluate the answer

(9) $\left(\frac{27}{125}\right)^{1/3}$

(10) $27^{1/3} \times 27$

(11) $\dfrac{27^{2/3} \times 16^{1/2} \times 4^{3/2}}{16^{1/4} \times 27^{1/3} \times 4}$

(12) $(16^{1/4})^3 \times (16^3)^{1/4}$

Negative powers and reciprocals

A negative power is often used to show that a term is being divided into another term. The sign before the dividing term is then a multiplication sign. For example, instead of writing

$$2^4 \div 2^2$$

we can write

$$2^4 \times 2^{-2}$$

which means exactly the same thing. In mathematics generally the negative sign is the opposite of the positive sign and indicates the opposite process to that indicated by the positive sign. Later on in algebra we shall be taking a positive sign to mean a movement along a line in a certain direction. A negative sign would then mean a movement along a line in the opposite direction. Similarly, in arithmetic if we say that we have 10 pence and spend 6 pence the amount remaining is $10 - 6$, that is 4 pence; and here the positive sign which is understood (but not shown) to precede the 10 indicates 'having' and the negative sign indicates 'spent' or 'no-longer having'.

With powers, a positive power in a term, for example

$$(3)^3 \times (2)^2$$

indicates that the term 3^3 is multiplied by the term 2^2 whereas a negative power, for example

$$(3)^3 \times (2)^{-2}$$

means that the term 3^3 is being *divided* by the term 2^2
so that

$$(3)^3 \times (2)^2 = 3^3 \times 2^2 \text{ that is } 3 \times 4$$

whereas

$$(3)^3 \times (2)^{-2} = \frac{3^3}{2^2} \text{ that is } \frac{3}{4}$$

Since 1×2^{-2} has exactly the same value as 2^{-2} it follows that

$$2^{-2} = 1 \times 2^{-2}$$
$$= \frac{1}{2^2}$$
$$= \frac{1}{4}$$

Also, since 2 can be written 2^1 (two raised to the power unity) then 2^{-1}, which equals 1×2^{-1}, must equal $1 \div 2$, that is 1/2.

The negative power unity is a special case and the term has a special name, the *reciprocal* of the number being raised to the power. For example

4^{-1} is the reciprocal of 4 and equals 1/4
5^{-1} is the reciprocal of 5 and equals 1/5
6^{-1} is the reciprocal of 6 and equals 1/6

Study the following examples and ensure that the meaning of the negative power is thoroughly understood.

Example 1.58

$$3^{-1} = \frac{1}{3}$$

Example 1.59

$$3^{-2} = \frac{1}{3^2} = \frac{1}{9}$$

Example 1.60

$$3^{-3} = \frac{1}{3^3} = \frac{1}{27}$$

Example 1.61

$$4^{-1} = \frac{1}{4}$$

Example 1.62

$$4^{-2} = \frac{1}{4^2} = \frac{1}{16}$$

Example 1.63

$$3 \times 6^{-2} = \frac{3}{6^2} = \frac{3}{36} \text{ or } \frac{1}{12} \text{ when simplified}$$

Example 1.64

$$5 \times 7^{-2} = \frac{5}{7^2} = \frac{5}{49}$$

Example 1.65

$$4^2 \times 5^{-2} = \frac{4^2}{5^2} = \frac{16}{25}$$

Example 1.66

$$3^3 \times 5^{-1} = \frac{3^3}{5} = \frac{27}{5} \text{ or } 5\frac{2}{5}$$

Example 1.67

$$5^2 \times 4^{-2} = \frac{5^2}{4^2} = \frac{25}{16} \text{ or } 1\frac{9}{16}$$

The last five examples contained two terms having different bases. Consider now some similar examples but having bases the same.

Example 1.68

$$4^3 \times 4^{-2} = \frac{4^3}{4^2} = 4^1 \text{ or } 4$$

Example 1.69

$$2^6 \times 2^{-3} = \frac{2^6}{2^3} = 2^3$$

Example 1.70

$$3^5 \times 3^{-7} = \frac{3^5}{3^7} = \frac{1}{3^2} \text{ or } 3^{-2}$$

Example 1.71

$$5^4 \times 5^{-5} = \frac{5^4}{5^5} = \frac{1}{5} \text{ or } 5^{-1} \text{ (the reciprocal of 5)}$$

These examples were worked out by writing the term with the negative power in the denominator. However, this need not be done provided one can manipulate positive and negative powers when they are to be added, subtracted or multiplied.

Consider again

$$4^3 \times 4^{-2}$$

Now the rule when multiplying terms containing the same base raised to a power is that the powers must be added. The first power is 3 and the second is −2. The resultant power is then $(3) + (-2)$ where the 3 is positive. As shown above the resultant power in this case is 1. That is

$$(3) + (-2) = 1.$$

This is logical since 3 is positive, 2 is negative and positive and negative are opposites. In this case +3 means a power of 3 in the numerator and −2 means a power of 2 in the denominator yielding a resultant power of 1 in the numerator. What has been done here is in fact an *addition* of two powers *taking into account their sign*. This is called an *algebraic addition*. (In this case since the first power was positive and the second negative, the algebraic addition turns out to be a subtraction that is $3 - 2$.)

Similarly with the remaining examples

$2^6 \times 2^{-3}$ resultant power is $6 - 3$, that is 3
$3^5 \times 3^{-7}$ resultant power is $5 - 7$, that is −2
$5^4 \times 5^{-5}$ resultant power is $4 - 5$, that is −1

The negative sign in the last two cases indicates that the final term lies in the denominator.

Note that this process of algebraic addition applies to the addition of any numbers having the same or different signs. In this case the numbers concerned were powers but in later chapters the numbers may take on other meanings.

The following example is of algebraic addition of powers where both are negative.

Example 1.72
Simplify $7^{-4} \times 7^{-5}$

This means
$$\frac{1}{7^4} \times \frac{1}{7^5}$$
that is
$$\frac{1}{7^4 \times 7^5}$$
$$= \frac{1}{7^{4+5}}$$
$$= \frac{1}{7^9}$$

This can be done directly by adding the first power (-4) to the second (-5), that is $(-4) + (-5)$ to give -9. In practical terms this means the first term has a power 4 in the denominator, the second term has a power 5 in the denominator so, since the same base is involved in each case, the resultant term has a power 9 in the denominator. (*Note.* The base *must* be the same.)

The following example is of *algebraic subtraction.*

Example 1.73
Simplify $5^7 \div 5^{-5}$

This means
$$5^7 \div \frac{1}{5^5}$$
which equals
$$5^7 \times 5^5$$
(changing the division sign to multiplication and turning upside down)
that is
$$5^{7+5}$$
$$= 5^{12}$$

The rule for division of terms containing a base raised to a power is that the power of the dividing term is *subtracted* from the power of the term being divided.

Clearly then $(7) - (-5) = 12$ from above and the effect of the minus sign outside the bracket containing the negative term is to turn it into a positive term. That is

$$(7) - (-5) = 7 + 5$$

Similarly

$$4^3 \div 4^{-2} = 4^{3+2}$$
$$= 4^5$$

and

$$3^6 \div 3^{-3} = 3^{6+3}$$
$$= 3^9$$

It can be seen that

$$4^3 \div 4^{-2} \text{ is the same as } 4^3 \times 4^2$$

and

$$3^6 \div 3^{-3} \text{ is the same as } 3^6 \times 3^3$$

that is the effect of a negative power on a division sign preceding the term containing the negative power is to turn it into a multiplication sign.

Finally consider multiple powers when one or more are negative.

Example 1.75

Simplify $(4^2)^{-3}$

This means

$$\frac{1}{(4^2)^3}$$

that is

$$\frac{1}{4^6}$$

applying the multiple-power rule to the denominator and $1/4^6$ can be written 4^{-6}. Thus

$$(4^2)^{-3} = 4^{-6}$$

and the left-hand power which by the rule of multiple powers is the *product* of the two, that is $(2) \times (-3)$, equals the right-hand power, that is -6. Thus

$$(2) \times (-3) = -6$$

The 2 here is positive, so this example shows that a positive power multiplied by a negative power yields a negative power.

As with the rule of algebraic addition and multiplication, this rule, which is for *algebraic multiplication*, that is multiplication taking the signs into consideration, applies to all numbers, whether they represent powers or not. This is considered again in a later chapter.

Now consider multiple powers when both are negative. Simplify

$$(4^{-2})^{-3}$$

This means

$$\left(\frac{1}{4^2}\right)^{-3}$$

and using the multiple-power rule derived above

$$\left(\frac{1}{4^2}\right)^{-3} = \frac{1}{4^{-6}}$$

Note. Both numerator and denominator are raised to the power indicated but the numerator remains unity since unity raised to any power positive or negative always remains the same.

Now

$$\frac{1}{4^{-6}} = \frac{1}{(1/4^6)}$$
$$= 4^6$$

So we see that

$$(4^{-2})^{-3} = 4^6$$

and thus, equating powers

$$(-2) \times (-3) = +6$$

that is a negative power multiplied by a negative power yields a positive power. Again this rule applies to all numbers during algebraic multiplication whether or not the numbers represent powers.

The rules determined for negative powers and their manipulation have been illustrated using only integer, that is not fractional, powers. However, they apply equally to fractional powers as shown below.

Example 1.76

Simplify $4^{2/3} \times 4^{-1/3}$

This equals

$$4^{2/3 - 1/3} \text{ that is } 4^{1/3} \text{ (cube root of 4)}$$

Example 1.77

Simplify $27^{-1/2} \times 27^{-1/2}$

This equals

$$27^{-1/2 - 1/2}$$

that is

$$27^{-1}$$

(since $-1/2 - 1/2 = -1$)

or

$$\frac{1}{27} \text{ (reciprocal of 27)}$$

Example 1.78
Simplify $(4^{-1/3})^4$

$$(4^{-1/3})^4 = 4^{-4/3} \text{ or } \frac{1}{4^{4/3}}$$

that is the reciprocal of the cube root of 4 raised to the power 4.

Example 1.79
Simplify $\left(\dfrac{2^{1/3}}{3}\right)^{-1/3}$

$$\left(\frac{2^{1/3}}{3}\right)^{-1/3} = \frac{2^{1/3 \times (-1/3)}}{3^{-1/3}}$$
$$= \frac{2^{-1/9}}{3^{-1/3}}$$
$$= \frac{3^{1/3}}{2^{1/9}}$$

that is the cube root of 3 divided by the ninth root of 2.

Example 1.80
Simplify $(2^3)^{-1/4} \times (2^4)^{1/3}$

Now
$$(2^3)^{-1/4} = 2^{-3/4} \text{ (using multiple powers)}$$
and
$$(2^4)^{1/3} = 2^{4/3} \text{ (using multiple powers)}$$
so that
$$(2^3)^{-1/4} \times (2^4)^{1/3} = 2^{-3/4} \times 2^{4/3}$$
$$= 2^{-3/4 + 4/3} \text{ (addition of powers)}$$
and since
$$-\frac{3}{4} + \frac{4}{3} = \frac{-9}{12} + \frac{16}{12}$$
$$= \frac{7}{12}$$
$$2^{-3/4 + 4/3} = 2^{7/12}$$
and the original expression
$$(2^3)^{1/4} \times (2^4)^{1/3} = 2^{7/12}$$
that is the twelfth root of 2 raised to the power 7.

This last example illustrates negative, multiple and fractional powers, addition of powers and algebraic addition of fractions. Careful examination of this example will prove most useful.

Exercise 1.6

Simplify the following

(1) $5^3 \times 125^{-1}$

(2) $4^{-3} \div 4^4$

(3) $\left(\dfrac{1}{3}\right)^{-2} \times \left(\dfrac{1}{9}\right)^{-4} \div \dfrac{1}{27}$

(4) $16^{-1/4} \times 4^{1/2} \div 2^{-1}$

(5) $49^{1/2} \times 343^{-1/3}$

(6) $\left(\dfrac{5}{8}\right)^{-1/3} \times \left(\dfrac{25}{64}\right)^{1/3}$

(7) $\left(\dfrac{4}{7}\right)^{5} \times \left(\dfrac{4}{7}\right)^{1/3} \div \left(\dfrac{49}{16}\right)^{1/2}$

(8) $(16^{-1/4} \div 16^{1/4} \times 16^{1/4})^{1/3}$

(9) $(3^2)^{1/3} \times (3^4)^{1/2}$

(10) $(4^5)^{1/2} \div (16^2)^{1/3}$

SYSTEMS OF NUMBERS

By far the most commonly used counting system is the decimal system.* This system uses as its basic number the number of digits on our two hands—eight fingers and two thumbs—and it is probable that this is the reason for the development of the system since, under normal circumstances, we carry a basic 'counting instrument' with us at all times. It is important to realise however, that the decimal system is only one of many possible systems, these being determined by the system basic number. There is for example the binary system, using two as its base, which is increasingly used in computer systems. It is also known that some primitive peoples, for example an Amazon tribe called the Yancos and the Temiar people of West Malaysia, use a tertiary system having three as its basic number.

All numbering systems whatever their basic number can be arranged in the same way and have similar characteristics concerning the number of available digits, their arrangement to signify a number greater than the basic number, and so on. The general rules are considered below with particular reference to the decimal and binary systems.

Number of digits

The number of digits, or 'figures' available, corresponds to the basic number. The basic number is also called the base or *radix* of the system. Thus the decimal system, radix ten, has ten digits 0, 1, 2, 3, 4, 5, 6, 7, 8, 9; the binary system, radix two, has two digits: 0 and 1. (Similarly a tertiary system, radix three, has digits 0, 1, 2 and an octal system, radix eight, would have digits 0, 1, 2, 3, 4, 5, 6, 7.)

Notice that for all systems there is no single figure to represent the radix, thus for the decimal system the radix ten is represented by 10, that is, a number using two of the basic digits 1 and 0. As we shall see shortly the radix is always represented by 10, and in our study of number systems we have to avoid the natural temptation of thinking of 10 as 'ten'. This is only true for the decimal system.

*The decimal system is also called the denary system.

Numbers larger than the base—order of digits

In any multi-digit number representing a total count greater than one the *least significant figure* is the one on the extreme right and represents the number of units in the total count. The number situated one place to the *left* of the least significant figure represents the number of times the radix is contained in the total count. Thus

for the decimal system 10 means 1 ten and 0 units
for the binary system 10 means 1 two and 0 units
for the octal system (radix eight) 10 means 1 eight and 0 units

Similarly

11 in the decimal system means 1 ten and 1 unit
11 in the binary system means 1 two and 1 unit

Clearly binary 11 means decimal three whereas decimal 11 means decimal eleven.
The figure situated two places to the left of the least significant figure represents the number of times the square of the radix is contained in the total count. Thus

for the decimal system 100 means 1 hundred 0 tens and 0 units
for the binary system 100 means 1 four 0 twos and 0 units
for the octal system 100 means 1 sixty-four 0 eights and 0 units

Notice that the words 'hundred', 'ten', 'two', 'sixty-four' apply to the decimal system since it is this system which is best understood. To appreciate this imagine that you have never heard of the decimal system, only of the binary system. The number 11 would not then be understood automatically as 'eleven' but as a number corresponding to decimal 'three'. All systems discussed must be referred to the best-known system—the decimal system—for the value of the count to be appreciated.
A further example of a three-digit number is 111 which

in decimal means 1 hundred 1 ten 1 unit
in binary means 1 four 1 two 1 unit (that is decimal seven)
in octal means 1 sixty-four, 1 eight, 1 unit (that is decimal seventy-three)

Similarly

decimal 101 means 1 hundred and 1
binary 101 means decimal five (1 four, 1 unit)
octal 101 means decimal sixty-five (1 sixty-four, 1 unit)

The figure situated three places to the left of the least significant figure represents the number of times the cube of the radix is repeated in the total count. Thus 1000 decimal means one thousand (ten cubed) no hundreds (ten squared), no tens, no units. 1000 binary means one eight (two cubed), no fours (two squared), no twos, no units.

In general, as one moves one place further to the left from the least significant figure the power of the radix is increased by one and in each case the figure tells us the number of times the radix raised to this power is repeated in the count. For example 10101 decimal means

> one ten-thousand (ten raised to the power four)
> no thousands (ten raised to the power three)
> one hundred (ten raised to the power two)
> no tens (ten raised to the power one)
> one unit (ten raised to the power nought)

that is ten thousand, one hundred and one
whereas 10101 binary means

> one sixteen (two raised to the power four)
> no eights (two raised to the power three)
> one four (two raised to the power two)
> no twos (two raised to the power one)
> one unit (two raised to the power nought)

that is (decimal) twenty-one.

Example 1.81
Write decimal 31 in binary.

Thirty-one contains 1 sixteen, 1 eight, 1 four, 1 two and 1 unit.
Thus decimal 31 = 1 1 1 1 1 binary.

Example 1.82
Write binary 1101101 in decimal.

The extreme figure on the left tells us the number of times the radix (2) raised to the power 6 is repeated in the count, the next figure to the *right* tells us the number of times the radix raised to the power 5 is repeated in the count. Thus binary 1101101 means

$$1 \times 2^6, 1 \times 2^5, 0 \times 2^4, 1 \times 2^3, 1 \times 2^2, 0 \times 2 \text{ and } 1 \text{ unit}$$

that is

$$2^6 + 2^5 + 2^3 + 2^2 + 1$$

or

$$64 + 32 + 8 + 4 + 1$$

which equals decimal 109.

Binary and decimal fractions

As was shown in the preceding section the order of digits, in numbers representing a count of greater than one, determines the number of times that powers of the radix are contained in the total count, the power increasing by one as the figure or digit moves one place to the left from the least significant figure. Exactly the same system may be used to set up a number describing a count of less than one, that is a fraction.

Some means must be used to indicate the break between those figures representing the number greater than one and those figures representing the fraction. Usually this break is indicated by a dot (or in some European countries a comma) called the *decimal point* for the decimal system, the *binary point* for the binary system, or in general the *radix point*. Thus where 110 for the decimal system means 1 hundred, 1 ten and 0 units, that is $1 \times (\text{ten})^2 + 1 \times (\text{ten})^1 + 0 \times (\text{ten})^0$ (remember that $(\text{ten})^0 = 1$) then, using a decimal point, the number

$$110.110$$

means

$$1 \times (\text{ten})^2 + 1 \times (\text{ten})^1 + 0 \times (\text{ten})^0 + 1 \times (\text{ten})^{-1} + 1 \times (\text{ten})^{-2} + 0 \times (\text{ten})^{-3}$$

and we see that the first figure to the *right* after the decimal point tells us the number of times the radix raised to the power -1 is repeated in the count, the second figure to the right tells us the number of times the radix raised to the power -2 is repeated in the count and so on.

Now

$$(\text{ten})^{-1} = \frac{1}{10}$$

$$(\text{ten})^{-2} = \frac{1}{100}$$

so the number 110.110 means

1 hundred, 1 ten, 0 units, 1 tenth, 1 hundredth and 0 thousandths

The last 0 is actually unnecessary.

Similarly the decimal number 2.934 means

2 units, 9 tenths, 3 hundredths and 4 thousandths

The same reasoning applied to the binary system indicates that binary 110.11 means

$$1 \times (\text{two})^2 + 1 \times (\text{two})^1 + 1 \times (\text{two})^0 + 1 \times (\text{two})^{-1} + 1 \times (\text{two})^{-2}$$

and since

$$
\begin{aligned}
2^2 &= 4 \\
2^1 &= 2 \\
2^0 &= 1 \\
2^{-1} &= 1/2 \\
2^{-2} &= 1/4
\end{aligned}
$$

binary 110.11 means

$$4 + 2 + 0 + \tfrac{1}{2} + \tfrac{1}{4}$$

that is $6\tfrac{3}{4}$ using a mixed number (whole number plus a proper fraction).

Example 1.83

Convert binary 1.11 to a mixed number.

Binary 1.11 means
$$(1 \times 2^0) + (1 \times 2^{-1}) + (1 \times 2^{-2})$$
that is
$$1 + \tfrac{1}{2} + \tfrac{1}{4}$$
which equals $1\tfrac{3}{4}$.

Example 1.84

Convert decimal 1.11 to a mixed number.

Decimal 1.11 means
$$(1 \times \text{ten}^0) + (1 \times \text{ten}^{-1}) + (1 \times \text{ten}^{-2})$$
that is
$$1 + \tfrac{1}{10} + \tfrac{1}{100}$$
which equals $1\tfrac{11}{100}$ (since $1/10 = 10/100$).

So far in this section we have examined the structure of a number and how the size and situation of each digit determines the value of the total count. This has been done for binary and decimal number-systems. The syllabuses for which this book is written require no further knowledge of the binary system at this stage and accordingly the rest of the section is devoted to the decimal system only. Manipulation and further consideration of binary numbers will be included in volume two of this series of texts.

MANIPULATION OF NUMBERS CONTAINING A DECIMAL POINT

Addition

If two or more numbers containing a decimal point are to be added, arrange the numbers one under the other with points in line and proceed as with whole numbers.

Example 1.85

Find the sum of 14.83, 13.7, 11.971.

$$
\begin{array}{r}
14.830 \\
13.700 \\
\underline{11.971} \\
\underline{40.501}
\end{array}
$$

To help keep the figures in line, noughts have been added to the end of each number. The addition of noughts after the decimal point (but *not* before) has no effect on the value of the number.

As shown, the answer is 40.501.

Example 1.86

Add 15, 14.7 and 13.21.

$$
\begin{array}{r}
15.00 \\
14.70 \\
\underline{13.21} \\
\underline{42.91}
\end{array}
$$

Note that the whole number 15 is written as 15.00.

Subtraction

If a number containing a decimal point is to be subtracted from another, arrange the numbers one beneath the other with points in line and proceed as with whole numbers.

Example 1.87

Find the difference between 9.76 and 12.53

$$
\begin{array}{r}
12.53 \\
\underline{9.76} \\
\underline{2.77}
\end{array}
$$

Example 1.88

Subtract 13.73 from 14

$$
\begin{array}{r}
14.00 \\
\underline{13.73} \\
\underline{0.27}
\end{array}
$$

Note that as with example 1.86, a whole number—in this case 14—is written as 14.00 to keep decimal points in line. The answer here is a decimal fraction 0.27. Using proper fractions this would be written as 27/100, that is 2/10 + 7/100 (see example 1.84).

Multiplication

Probably the easiest method of multiplication is to convert the figures concerned to whole numbers, multiply in the usual way and determine the position of the decimal point in the answer at the conclusion of the multiplication. First it is necessary to examine the effect of multiplying a number containing a decimal point by ten or powers of ten. Consider

$$34.7 \times 10$$

Now 34.7 means 34 and 7/10 as shown earlier.

Multiplying 34 by ten yields 340 and 7/10 by ten yields 7.

Hence
$$34.7 \times 10 = 340 + 7$$
$$= 347$$
which may be written 347.0 and we see that the decimal point moves one place to the *right* when multiplying by 10.

Thus for example
$$13.93 \times 10 = 139.3$$
$$43.742 \times 10 = 437.42$$

and so on.

Similarly, when multiplying by 10^2, that is 100, the decimal point moves two places to the right. To show this, consider

$$12.73 \times 100$$

Now 12.73 can be written 12 and 73/100
Thus
$$100 \times 12\tfrac{73}{100} = 1200 + 73$$
$$= 1273$$

In general, when multiplying by ten raised to a power move the decimal point a number of places to the right equal to the power; that is one for a multiplier of 10, two for a multiplier of 100 (10^2), three for 1000 (10^3) and so on.

At this point it could be noted that the opposite process takes place when dividing, in that the decimal point is moved to the *left* by a number of places equal to the power to which ten is raised in the dividing number; that is one place when dividing by 10, two places when dividing by 100, three places when dividing by 1000 and so on.

To return to multiplication, consider the following example.

Example 1.80
Evaluate 1.25×3.5

First multiply 125×35 in the usual way

```
    125
     35
    625
   375
   4375
```

The problem was 1.25×3.5, the answer 4375 is that of the problem 125×35. Clearly

1.25 has been multiplied by 100
3.5 has been multiplied by 10

The answer 4375 is thus 10×100 times too large. To divide 4375 by 10×100, that is 1000, write 4375 as 4375.0 and move the decimal point *three* places to the *left* (three since the dividing number is 1000, that is 10^3).
This gives 4.375. Thus

$$1.25 \times 3.5 = 4.475$$

In general, when multiplying two numbers containing decimal points, count the number of figures *after* the point in each number and add these numbers of figures. Convert the numbers in the problem to whole numbers, multiply out and locate the decimal point in the answer by moving the point to the left, a number of times equal to the total number of figures after the decimal point in the numbers being multiplied. The process is easier to demonstrate than describe in words. Study the following examples.

Example 1.90
Evaluate 4.2×3.14

$$
\begin{array}{r}
42 \\
314 \\
\hline
168 \\
42 \\
126 \\
\hline
13188
\end{array}
$$

There is one figure after the decimal point in 4.2 and two figures after the decimal point in 3.14, that is *three* figures in all.
Write 13188 as 13188.0 and move the point *three* places to the left giving 13.188. Thus

$$4.2 \times 3.14 = 13.188$$

Example 1.91
Evaluate $4.1 \times 5.6 \times 2.35$

First two numbers

$$
\begin{array}{r}
41 \\
56 \\
\hline
246 \\
205 \\
\hline
2296
\end{array}
$$

Now multiplying by 235

```
       2296
        235
      11480
       6888
       4592
     539560
```

In 4.1 there is one figure after the point, in 5.6 there is one figure and in 2.35 there are two figures after the point, that is a total of four figures.

Write 539560 as 539560.0 and move the point four places to the left, giving the answer 53.956.

Division

When dividing one number into another and one or both contain a decimal point, the most convenient method is to move the point in *both* numbers until the dividing number is converted to a whole number. No adjustment of the answer is necessary, since provided the point is moved the same number of places in the same direction in both numbers, the answer remains the same.

For example 12.3/4.1 has the same value as 123/41, since 12.3 has been multiplied by 10 to give 123 and 4.1 has been multiplied by 10 to give 41, that is multiplication of numerator (12.3) and denominator (4.1) by the same figure (10) leaves the answer unchanged.

Example 1.92

Divide 34.644 by 1.2

This is the same as dividing 346.44 by 12

```
          28.87
    12/346.44
       24
       106
        96
       104
        96
        84
        84
         0
```

The answer is 28.87.

Note. The decimal point in the answer lies immediately *above* the point in the number being divided when this layout of the solution is used.

Example 1.93

Divide 25.74 by 1.5

Now

$$\frac{25.74}{1.5} = \frac{257.4}{15}$$

$$
\begin{array}{r}
17.16 \\
15\overline{)257.4} \\
\underline{15} \\
107 \\
\underline{105} \\
24 \\
\underline{15} \\
90 \\
\underline{90} \\
\underline{00}
\end{array}
$$

The answer is 17.16.

Note. When no further figures are available to be brought down a nought is used. Thus in example 1.93 when 15 is subtracted from 24 leaving the remainder 9 a nought is placed after the 9 to give 90 and the dividing process is continued until there is no remainder. This is quite in order since 257.4 can just as correctly be written 257.400. Sometimes, the process may continue indefinitely with a remainder always present. Consider the following example.

Example 1.94

$2.2 \div 0.7$

This is the same as $22 \div 7$. Using long division (which is not really necessary) we get

$$
\begin{array}{r}
3.14285 \\
7\overline{)22.0} \\
\underline{21} \\
10 \\
\underline{7} \\
30 \\
\underline{28} \\
20 \\
\underline{14} \\
60 \\
\underline{56} \\
40 \\
\underline{35} \\
50 \text{ etc.}
\end{array}
$$

In this example the dividing process continues indefinitely and the answer is determined by the degree of accuracy required. This is discussed below.

Approximations

Two phrases are of particular importance when using decimal notation. These are 'places of decimals' and 'significant figures'. The number of places of decimals or significant figures in an answer of the kind found in the previous example determine its accuracy. When such an answer is reduced to a few figures an *approximation* has been made.

The phrase 'places of decimals' is self explanatory and refers to the number of figures following the decimal point. For example, consider the number (written to four places of decimals) 3.1428. If we wish to write this to three places we have to decide what the third figure following the point should be to obtain a reasonable degree of accuracy. Since 3.1428 is closer in value to 3.143 than 3.142 then 3.143 would be the correct answer to three places. In general the rule is: if the figure following the figure in the last place required lies between 5 and 9, the last figure is increased by 1; if not it remains as it is.

Example 1.95
Express the following decimal numbers to the number of places of decimals shown.

(a) 53.678 to 2 places   (b) 1.78 to 1 place
(c) 1.597 to 2 places   (d) 1.594 to 2 places

(a) The figure in the third place is 8, change the preceding 7 to 8—answer is 53.68.
(b) The figure in the second place is 8, change the preceding 7 to 8—answer is 1.8.
(c) The figure in the third place is 7, change the preceding 9 to 10 which in turn changes the 5 to 6—answer is 1.60.
(d) The figure in the third place is 4. Leave the preceding 9 at 9—answer is 1.59.

The phrase 'significant figures' means the number of figures other than zero which in total make up the number, regardless of whether the figures lie before or after the point. The same rule of approximation applies as above.
For example

19.35 to 3 significant figures is 19.4
19.35 to 2 significant figures is 19

1.985 to 3 significant figures is 1.99
1.985 to 2 significant figures is 2.0

1273.5 to 3 significant figures is 1270
1273.5 to 2 significant figures is 1300

Standard form—powers of ten

Writing a decimal number in standard form means having only one figure before
the decimal point and adjusting the overall value to that required using a
multiplier of ten raised to the appropriate power.

Example 1.96

Express in standard form
(a) 198.3   (b) 17.53   (c) 5726.5   (d) 0.534

(a) $198.3 = 1.983 \times 100$ that is 1.983×10^2
(b) $17.53 = 1.753 \times 10$
(c) $5726.5 = 5.7265 \times 1000$ that is 5.7265×10^3
(d) $0.534 = 5.34/10$ that is 5.34×10^{-1}

Standard form is particularly useful when estimating an answer.
For example, evaluate
$$\frac{19.7 \times 1.8 \times 5613}{4.9 \times 35.1}$$
This can be written
$$\frac{1.97 \times 10 \times 1.8 \times 5.613 \times 10^3}{4.9 \times 3.51 \times 10}$$
that is
$$\frac{1.97 \times 1.8 \times 5.613}{4.9 \times 3.51} \times 10^3$$
when tens are cancelled.
This is approximately
$$\frac{2 \times 2 \times 6}{5 \times 4} \times 10^3$$
that is
$$\frac{24000}{20} \text{ or } 1200$$
(The actual answer is 1157.26)

Estimation of this sort is usually used when the order of magnitude of an
answer is required. Often the actual figures (in this case 1157.26) are determined
by some other means, for example a slide rule (discussed in chapter 2).

Powers of 10 are commonly used as a multiplier to reduce or increase a
number to a reasonable size. When used, a prefix is attached to the unit of
whatever is being measured to indicate the power of 10. A list of prefixes and
their abbreviations follows.

Multiplier	Prefix	Abbreviation	Multiplier	Prefix	Abbreviation
10^{12}	tera	T	10^{-12}	pico	p
10^9	giga	G	10^{-9}	nano	n
10^6	mega	M	10^{-6}	micro	μ
10^3	kilo	k	10^{-3}	milli	m
10^2	hecto	h	10^{-2}	centi	c
10	deca	da	10^{-1}	deci	d

For example

a current of 0.0135 ampères is expressed as 13.5 milliampères (abbreviated mA) since $0.0135 = 13.5 \times 10^{-3}$

a voltage of 5673 volts is expressed as 5.673 kilovolts (abbreviated kV) since $5673 = 5.673 \times 10^3$

a resistance of 5 600 000 ohms is expressed as 5.6 megohms (abbreviated MΩ) since $5\ 600\ 000 = 5.6 \times 10^6$

In cases like this it is usual to stop dividing when a sufficiently accurate answer is obtained. Accuracy and estimation are considered in chapter 2.

Conversion of proper fractions to decimal fractions

Long or short division may be used to convert a proper fraction to a decimal fraction. In example 1.94 we saw 22/7 converted to 3.1428 etc.
Similarly

$$\frac{3}{7} = 0.428 \text{ etc.}$$

by dividing 7 into 3.000.

$$\frac{2}{5} = 0.4$$

by dividing 5 into 2.0.

$$\frac{5}{8} = 0.625$$

by dividing 8 into 5.000.
Also

$$3\tfrac{3}{7} = 3.428$$

either by writing $3\tfrac{3}{7}$ as 24/7 and dividing 24.00 by 7 or by putting the whole number 3 before the point of the decimal fraction 0.428 (which equals 3/7).
Similarly

$$4\tfrac{2}{5} = 4.4$$

either by evaluating 22/5 or placing 4 before 0.4, and

$$3\tfrac{5}{8} = 3.625$$

either by evaluating 29/8 or by placing 3 before 0.625.

Conversion of decimal fractions to proper fractions

Example 1.97

Convert the following to proper fractions or mixed numbers as appropriate
(a) 0.76   (b) 0.125   (c) 3.5   (d) 56.625   (e) 1.28

(a) 0.76 $= \dfrac{76}{100}$

$= \dfrac{19}{25}$ (dividing through by 4)

(b) 0.125 $= \dfrac{125}{1000}$

$= \dfrac{1}{8}$ (dividing through by 125)

(c) 3.5 $= \dfrac{35}{10}$

$= \dfrac{7}{2}$ (dividing through by 5)

$= 3\frac{1}{2}$

(d) 56.625 $= 56 + 0.625$

$= 56 + \dfrac{625}{1000}$

$= 56 + \dfrac{5}{8}$ (dividing fraction through by 125)

$= 56\frac{5}{8}$

(e) 1.28 $= \dfrac{128}{100}$

$= \dfrac{34}{25}$

$= 1\frac{9}{25}$

Percentages

The numerator of a fraction containing 100 as the denominator is called a
percentage. Thus for example 43 per cent (written 43%) means 43/100. A
percentage figure is usually used to indicate a part of a whole, as for example in
the statement '43 per cent of the students passed the examination'. This means
43/100 of the number of students taking the examination were successful. Thus
if 100 students took the examination

$$\frac{43}{100} \text{ of 100 that is } \frac{43}{100} \times 100$$

or

43 students passed

Similarly, if 200 students took the examination and 43 per cent passed, then

$$\frac{43}{100} \times 200$$

that is 86 students were successful.

Any fraction, proper, improper or decimal may be converted to a percentage.

Example 1.98

Convert the following to percentages

(a) 2/5   (b) 3/4   (c) 0.47   (d) 0.073   (e) 3/7

(a) $\frac{2}{5} = \frac{40}{100}$ (multiplying through by 20)

$$= 40\%$$

Thus $\frac{2}{5}$ of any number means 40 per cent of that number.

(b) $\frac{3}{4} = \frac{75}{100}$

$$= 75\%$$

(c) $0.47 = \frac{47}{100}$

$$= 47\%$$

(d) $0.073 = \frac{73}{1000}$

$$= \frac{7.3}{100}$$

$$= 7.3\%$$

(e) Since 100 is not exactly divisible by the denominator 7 convert to a decimal fraction

$$\frac{3}{7} = 0.4285 \text{ (to 4 places)}$$

$$= \frac{42.85}{100}$$

$$= 42.85\%$$

Exercise 1.7

(1)   Convert binary 11011 to decimal

(2)   Convert binary 11.11 to decimal

(3)   Express as decimal fractions to 3 decimal places (a) 7/8 (b) 5/9 (c) 10/11
      (d) 7/10

(4) Evaluate the following to two decimal places
    (a)   25.6 + 13.7 +14.19   (f) $14.8\,(13.7 - 5.9) \div 13.7$
    (b)   13.3 + 8.7 − 5.1   (g) $18.9 \times 3.75 \div 1.4$
    (c)   13.5 − 8.6 + 2.3   (h) $1.73\,(15.64 - 13.2 + 9.7)$
    (d) $13.5\,(14.6 - 13.2)$ (i) $8.4\,(3.65)^2$
    (e) $18.75 + 12\,(17.6 \times 1.5)$ (j) $24.76 - (4.21)^2$

(5) Evaluate the following to two decimal places
    (a) $\dfrac{18.75 \times 14}{43.2}$ (c) $\left(\dfrac{14.8 \times 14.1}{3.7}\right)^2$

    (b) $\dfrac{76.57 \times 3.49}{2.5 \times 7.2}$ (d) $\left(\dfrac{13.9 \times 12.3 \times 14.7}{5.65 \times 7.9}\right)^3$

(6) Convert the following to percentages to two decimal places
    (a) 4/9   (b) 0.5   (c) 3/11   (d) 0.713

(7) (a)   Express 0.578 A in milliamps
    (b)   Express 53.7 mA in amps
    (c)   Express 0.41 μV in volts
    (d)   Express 0.000275 V in microvolts
    (e)   Express 5 760 000 Ω in megohms

(8) Is 2/3 of 20% of 512 greater than or less than 1/5 of 70% of 145?

(9) (a)   write the following numbers to 3 significant figures
           31.75; 43.21; 732.8; 0.695; 1.984
    (b)   Write the numbers in (a) to 2 decimal places

(10) Estimate the value of the following (a considerable degree of variation is
     allowed but the order of magnitude must be correct).
    (a) $\dfrac{3174 \times 512}{678}$ (b) $\dfrac{39.7 \times 4.5}{7.2 \times 8.9}$ (c) $\dfrac{0.013 \times 0.0056}{0.0078 \times 0.2}$

2 Aids to Calculations

If the reader has completed exercise 1.7, particularly question 5, the amount of tedious work involved in working out problems in arithmetic using long division and multiplication will be obvious. Fortunately other quicker methods have been developed, including tables of logarithms, roots and reciprocals and the slide rule.

LOGARITHMS

In chapter 1 we saw that when numbers consisting of a base raised to a power are multiplied or divided, the powers are added or subtracted respectively, provided that the base is the same throughout. Addition and subtraction are far easier processes to carry out than multiplication and division, particularly where large numbers are involved. The idea behind logarithms is to express numbers in terms of a power to which a base is raised. These powers may then be added or subtracted if the original numbers are to be multiplied or divided. Logarithms are thus powers of a common base. Any base may be used but the most common one is 10.

A second base often encountered in more advanced mathematics is 2.718, which produced 'out of the blue' so to speak, seems a peculiar number. The constant 2.718 occurs repeatedly in electrical and electronic theory and logarithms taking this number as their base are called natural or Naperian logarithms. We shall confine ourselves to logarithms to the base 10 in this chapter.

To clarify the theory behind logarithms consider the simple multiplication problem

10 000 × 1000

This hardly requires any mechanical aids but is useful to demonstrate logarithm theory.

10 000 may be written 10^4
1000 may be written 10^3

49

Thus

$$10\,000 \times 1000 = 10^4 \times 10^3$$
$$= 10^{4+3} \qquad \text{(addition of powers)}$$
$$= 10^7$$
$$= 10\,000\,000 \qquad \text{(ten million)}$$

Suppose instead of writing 10 000 as 10^4 we write it as 4. We are then describing the number (10 000) in terms of the power (4) to which a base (10) is raised; that is

4 is the logarithm of 10 000 to the base 10

Similarly

3 is the logarithm of 1000 to the base 10

and thus

7 is the logarithm of 10 000 × 1000 to the base 10

In the problem 10 000 ÷ 1000 we can write

$$10\,000 \div 1000 = 10^4 \div 10^3$$
$$= 10^{4-3}$$
$$= 10^1$$
$$= 10$$

and we see that

1 is the logarithm of $\dfrac{10\,000}{1000}$ to the base 10

It is clear then that if numbers can be expressed as powers, these powers may be added or subtracted if the original numbers are to be multiplied or divided.

Of course the problems so far demonstrated are easy and require little effort. This is because the numbers concerned were whole numbers and whole-number powers of 10, that is 4, 3, etc. Where logarithms prove extremely useful is when the numbers involved are not whole numbers and are not whole-number powers of 10.

Before we examine manipulation of logarithms further let us consider what value of logarithm we might expect for different numbers. We know that

$$10^1 = 10$$
$$10^2 = 100$$
$$100^3 = 1000$$

and so on.
Thus

the logarithm of 10 to the base 10 is 1
and of 100 is 2
and of 1000 is 3

Suppose we wanted the logarithm of 20, that is we want the power to which 10 is raised to equal 20. We know that 10 raised to the power 1 equals 10 and raised to the power 2 equals 100. We might expect then that the power to which 10 must be raised to equal 20, that is the logarithm of 20 to the base 10, will lie between 1 and 2.

From tables of logarithms it is seen that in fact the logarithm of 20 to the base 10 is 1.301. (The reader is asked to accept this for the moment until after we have studied how to read the tables.) Thus 10 raised to the power 1.301 equals 20, that is

$$10^{1.301} = 20$$

The natural question that presents itself here is what does a power of 1.301 mean? We have seen that 10^1 means 10 and that 10^2 means 10×10 but on first sight $10^{1.301}$ is inexplicable using the simple rules of powers.

However 1.301 can be written as 1301/1000 using the rules of decimals examined in chapter 1 and thus $10^{1.301}$ means $10^{1301/1000}$ where 1301/1000 is a fractional power. Applying the rules of fractional powers, this tells us that

$$10^{1301/1000}$$

means the thousandth root of 10 raised to the power 1301, that is the number which when multiplied by itself 999 times $(1000 - 1)$ equals 10 multiplied by itself 1300 times $(1301 - 1)$. This number is 20. In other words

$$20^{1000} = 10^{1301}$$

or

$$20 \quad = 10^{1301/1000}$$

or

$$20 \quad = 10^{1.301}$$

and the logarithm of 20 to the base 10 is 1.301. In addition, as we can see that 20 lies between 10 and 100 and 10 is 10^1 and 100 is 10^2, then the power to which 10 is raised to equal 20 lies between 1 and 2.

Similarly, since 200 lies between 100 (which is 10^2) and 1000 (which is 10^3) then the power to which 10 must be raised to equal 200, that is the logarithm of 200 to the base 10, must lie between 2 and 3.

It follows that the logarithm of 2000 lies between 3 and 4 since 2000 lies between 1000 (10^3) and 10 000 (10^4), and the logarithm of 20 000 lies between 4 and 5, and so on. In other words as the number is increased tenfold, the figure preceding the decimal point in the logarithm rises by 1. This figure is given a name – the *characteristic* of the logarithm.

Another useful aspect of using 10 as the base of a system of logarithms is shown below.

We have seen that
$$\log_{10} 20 = 1.301$$

This means
$$20 = 10^{1.301}$$
Now
$$200 = 20 \times 10$$
$$= 10^{1.301} \times 10^1$$
$$= 10^{2.301}$$
and thus
$$\log 200 = 2.301$$
Similarly
$$2000 = 20 \times 100$$
$$= 10^{1.301} \times 10^2$$
$$= 10^{3.301}$$
and thus
$$\log 2000 = 3.301$$
It follows that
$$\log 20\ 000 = 4.301$$
$$\log 200\ 000 = 5.301$$
$$\log 2\ 000\ 000 = 6.301$$
and so on. As we can see the characteristic of all these logarithms increases by 1 as the number is increased tenfold. This was shown earlier in another way. The essential point however is that the part of the logarithm following the decimal point (0.301) remains the same for all these numbers 20, 200, 2000, etc. This part of a logarithm is called the *mantissa*.

In general the mantissa is the same for all numbers having the same figures in the same order — only the characteristic changes. The value of the characteristic may be determined by a simple rule — it is one *less* than the total number of figures (if any) preceding the decimal point in the number whose logarithm is being found.
Thus
$$20 \text{ has two figures — characteristic } 1, \text{ mantissa } .301$$
$$200 \text{ has three figures — characteristic } 2, \text{ mantissa } .301$$
$$2000 \text{ has four figures — characteristic } 3, \text{ mantissa } .301$$

We can now examine tables of logarithms.

(Note how a logarithm is written; if desired the 10 may be omitted and it is understood that, unless otherwise stated, the base is 10.)

Example 2.1

Find the logarithm of the following numbers
    (a) 30   (b) 300   (c) 15.6   (d) 156   (e) 13.23   (f) 1.3

Tables of logarithms give only the mantissa, the characteristic is determined by the method described above.

(a) Look down the left-hand column on the far side of the page until 30 is reached. Move along the line to the column headed 0. The figure is 4771. The mantissa is thus .4771. The number has two figures preceding the decimal point (the decimal point in the number 30 is not shown, but 30 can be written 30.0); thus the characteristic is 1 less than 2, that is 1.

$$\log 30 = 1.4771$$

(b) The mantissa of log 300 is the same as that of log 30 and was found in (a). The characteristic is different and is 2 since 300 contains three figures.

$$\log 300 = 2.4771$$

(c) Look down the left-hand column as before until 15 is reached. Move along the line to the column headed 6. The mantissa is .1931. The number of figures before the decimal point in 15.6 is two; the characteristic is thus 1.

$$\log 15.6 = 1.1931$$

(d) The mantissa of log 156 is the same as for 15.6. The characteristic however is increased to 2.

$$\log 156 = 2.1931$$

(e) Look down the left-hand column until 13 is reached. Move along the line to the column headed 2. This gives 1206 but is not the required mantissa since the number has a fourth figure (3). Move along the line until, in the second batch of columns at the right-hand side of the page, the column headed 3 is reached. The number is 10. Add this to 1206 to give 1216. The mantissa of log 13.23 is .1216. The characteristic using the rules given above is 1.

$$\log 13.23 = 1.1216$$

(f) Look down the left-hand column until 13 is reached. Move along the line to the column headed 0. The mantissa is .1139. The number is 1.3 and the number of figures preceding the decimal point is one, 1 less than 1 is 0. Thus 0 is the characteristic.

$$\log 1.3 = 0.1139$$

Exercise 2.1

Find the logarithms of the following

(a) 4.6	(b) 46	(c) 32.3	(d) 32.34	(e) 3.234
(f) 78.94	(g) 789.4	(h) 7894	(i) 2.763	(j) 27.63

The following example illustrates the use of logarithms.

Example 2.2

Evaluate 15.6 × 13.23

The logarithms of these numbers were found in example 2.1 When numbers are multiplied their logarithms are added to give the logarithm of the answer.

Number	Log
15.6	1.1931
13.23	1.1216
	2.3147

Thus

2.3147 is the logarithm of (15.6 × 13.23)

To find the number corresponding to this logarithm the tables may be used in reverse, that is looking in the logarithm columns until the mantissa .3147 is found. An easier method is to use *antilogarithm tables* which are usually provided with logarithm tables.

Remember that logarithm tables give only the mantissa. Thus, it is the mantissa we locate in the antilogarithm tables. The mantissa is .3147. Look down the left-hand column until .31 is reached, move along the line to column headed 4. Read off 2061. Move along the line to the next set of columns at the right-hand side of the page until the column headed 7 is reached. Read off 3. Add 3 to 2061 to give 2064. The figures and order of figures of the number having the logarithm 2.3147 are thus given by 2064.

The next question is where the decimal point is to be placed. The characteristic of 2.3147 is 2 which tells us that there are three figures before the decimal point in the number having 2.3147 as its logarithm.
Thus

2.3147 is the logarithm of 206.4

and

15.6 × 13.23 = 206.4

It will be appreciated that once the use of logarithm and antilogarithm tables is mastered, the work involved in solving a problem of the type shown is much less using logarithms than using ordinary multiplication.

The following examples should be carefully studied.

Example 2.3
Evaluate 12.95 × 1.37 × 53.67

Number	Log	
12.95	1.1123	
1.37	0.1367	Addition
53.67	1.7298	
952.3	2.9788	

the answer is 952.3

Example 2.4

Evaluate 12.95 × 1.37 ÷ 5.367

Number	Log	
12.95	1.1123	
1.37	0.1367	Addition
	1.2490	
5.367	0.7298	Subtraction
3.306	0.5192	

the answer is 3.306

Example 2.5

Evaluate $17.57^3 \times 9.71^2$

Here, one number is cubed, that is multiplied by itself twice. Thus the logarithm of the cubed number is the result of adding the logarithm of the number to itself twice, that is three times the logarithm of the number. Similarly, the logarithm of 9.71^2 is 2 × logarithm of 9.71.

	Number	Log	
	17.57	1.2447	
	17.57^3	3.7341	that is 3 × 1.2447
	9.71	0.9872	
	9.71^2	1.9744	that is 2 × 0.9872
Answer	511100	5.7085	(Add 3.7341 to 1.9744)

Note in this example the antilog of 7085 yields 5111. The characteristic of the log of the answer is 5 which tells us there are six figures preceding the decimal point in the answer. Thus two noughts are added to give 511 100.0 or as written 511 100.

Logarithms of numbers less than 1

The fact that the mantissa in logarithms of all numbers having the same figures in the same order remains the same is most useful. It means that only one set of tables is required to provide the mantissa for the range of numbers from 1 to 99.99, the characteristic of the logarithm being determined separately.* The same idea can be applied to logarithms of numbers less than 1, that is decimal fractions, provided that use is made of negative characteristics.

* The left-hand column reads from 10 to 99 but for numbers in the range 1–10 the column is read as 1.0 to 9.9.

Example 2.6

Find the logarithm of 0.5012.

Now

$$0.5012 = \frac{5.012}{10}$$

that is

$$10^{-1} \times 5.012$$

The logarithm of 5.012 using tables is 0.7
This means

$$10^{0.7} = 5.012$$

Thus

$$0.5012 = 10^{-1} \times 10^{0.7}$$

since $10^{-1} = 1/10$

$$= 10^{-1+0.7}$$

We see then that 10 raised to the power $-1+0.7$ is equal to 0.5012 and thus the logarithm of 0.5012 to the base 10 is $-1+0.7$. Let us examine this logarithm or power more closely. $-1+0.7$ as a power represents a negative power (which means a dividing number or denominator) and a positive power (which means a multiplying number or numerator). $-1+0.7$ can be written as -0.3 since the negative power 1 exceeds the positive power 0.7 by 0.3 and this would then be a wholly negative power which tells us that

$$0.5012 = 10^{-0.3}$$

$$= 1/10^{0.3}$$

that is the reciprocal of $10^{0.3}$ or, since $10^{0.3} = 10^{3/10}$, the reciprocal of the tenth root of 10^3. If we use $10^{-0.3}$ then -0.3 is the logarithm of 0.5012 and the mantissa of this logarithm (.3) is not then the same as the mantissa of the logarithms of 5.012, 50.12, 501.2, etc. In other words we should need a new set of tables for logarithms of numbers less than 1.

However if we use $-1+0.7$, the decimal-fraction part of the logarithm is the same as the mantissa of all the other logarithms of numbers containing the figures 5, 0, 1, 2 in that order. Consequently, the logarithm is written as $\bar{1}.7$ (described as 'bar one-point-seven') where $\bar{1}$ means a characteristic of minus 1. The mantissa is positive.

Example 2.7

Find the logarithm of (a) 0.05012, (b) 0.005012.

(a) Now

$$0.05012 = \frac{5.012}{100}$$

$$= 10^{0.7} \times 10^{-2}$$

Thus
$$\log 0.05012 = \bar{2}.7 \text{ (bar two-point-seven)}$$

(b)
$$0.005012 = \frac{5.012}{1000}$$
$$= 10^{0.7} \times 10^{-3}$$

Thus
$$\log 0.005012 = \bar{3}.7 \text{ (bar three-point-seven)}$$

In general for numbers less than 1 the logarithm has a positive mantissa, obtained from tables in the usual way, and a negative characteristic equal to one more than the number of noughts following the decimal point and before the figures other than nought begin.

To recapitulate
$$\log 0.5012 = \bar{1}.7$$
since there are no noughts between the point and the first figure (5) in the number the characteristic of the logarithm is -1 written $\bar{1}$
$$\log 0.05012 = \bar{2}.7$$
there is one nought between the point and 5, the characteristic is -2.
$$\log 0.005012 = \bar{3}.7$$
there are two noughts between the point and 5, the characteristic is -3.

Example 2.8

Find the logarithms of
(a) 5.74   (b) 0.574   (c) 0.0574   (d) 0.345   (e) 0.076   (f) 0.0005

    (a) $\log 5.74 = 0.7589$ from tables (look up 574)
    (one figure before the decimal point, characteristic one less, equals 0)
    (b) $\log 0.574 = \bar{1}.7589$
    (no noughts after the decimal point, characteristic one more and negative)
    (c) $\log 0.0574 = \bar{2}.7589$
    (one nought after the decimal point, characteristic one more and negative)
    (d) $\log 0.345 = \bar{1}.5378$ (mantissa obtained by looking up 345)
    (e) $\log 0.076 = \bar{2}.8808$ (mantissa obtained by looking up 76)
    (f) $\log 0.0005 = \bar{4}.6990$ (mantissa obtained by looking up 5)

When the antilogarithm of a logarithm with a negative characteristic is required, the mantissa is used in conjunction with antilogarithm tables to find the figures in the number corresponding to the given logarithm. The value of the characteristic is used to determine the position of the decimal point, that is if the characteristic is bar-one the decimal point lies immediately preceding the figures, if the characteristic is bar-two one nought lies between the point and the figures and so on.

For example, antilog $\bar{2}.8808$ (example 2.8e above): the mantissa .8808 yields the figures 7586 + 14, that is 76 from tables. The characteristic $\bar{2}$ indicates one nought preceding this, thus antilog $\bar{2}.8808 = 0.076$.

In the manipulation of logarithms of numbers less than 1, great care must be taken and it must always be remembered that while the characteristic is negative the mantissa is *always* positive. Since the sign must be taken into consideration any addition or subtraction which takes place must be algebraic. The basic rules of algebraic addition and subtraction were explained in chapter 1, pp. 28–9.

Consider the following examples

Example 2.9

Evaluate 0.573 × 0.94.

Number	Log
0.573	$\bar{1}.7582$
0.940	$\bar{1}.9731$
0.5387	$\bar{1}.7313$

In the addition of the two logarithms the process continues in the normal fashion until the figures immediately following the decimal point; that is 2 plus 1 equals 3, 8 plus 3 equals 11 — put down 1 carry 1 and so on until we reach 7 plus 9 equals 16 — put down 6 carry 1. The 1 that is carried here is *positive* since it exists as a result of adding two parts of positive mantissae.

To add characteristics we thus have $-1-1+1$ which equals -1 and is written $\bar{1}$ in the sum of the two logarithms. Thus the mantissa of this sum .7313 yields 5387 in antilogarithm tables and $\bar{1}$ puts the decimal point immediately preceding the 5 to give 0.5387 as the answer.

Example 2.10

Evaluate 0.573 ÷ 0.94

The logarithms required in this example are the same as those in the previous example

Number	Log
0.5730	$\bar{1}.7582$
0.9400	$\bar{1}.9731$
0.6096	$\bar{1}.7851$

The explanation of the process of subtraction when negative characteristics are involved depends upon how the reader was taught subtraction of numbers from smaller numbers. For example, consider the first occasion this occurs in example 2.10. This is when it becomes necessary to subtract 7 from 5.

One method of approach is to subtract 7 from 15 (leaving 8) thus 'borrowing' 10 from the next column and then to compensate for the borrowed 10 by increasing the 9 in the next column (lower figure) to 10. The other method is to borrow 10 as before, take 7 from 15 (leaving 8) but this time to compensate by reducing the 7 in the next column (upper figure) to 6. Thus in the first method the next stage of the calculation involves taking 10 from 7 while the second method involves taking 9 from 6 as the next part of the calculation. Either way we again have the problem of taking a large number from a smaller but with the added complication of negative characteristics in the next column of figures.

Consider method one: we have to subtract 10 from 7. Borrow 10 to make 7 into 17, subtract 10 from 17 leaving 7 as the remainder. Now add 1 to the lower figure in the next column. This lower figure is -1. Add 1 to -1, that is $-1+1$ which leaves 0. Now subtract this figure 0 from the upper figure -1 giving $-1-0 = -1$, that is bar-one ($\bar{1}$) as the characteristic of the logarithm of the answer.

Alternatively, we have to subtract 9 from 6, so borrow 10 to make 6 into 16, subtract 9 leaving 7 as the remainder. Now reduce the upper figure in the next column by 1. The upper figure (bar-one) is -1. To reduce by 1 subtract 1 from this, giving $-1-1$, that is -2 (bar-two) as the characteristic. Now subtract the lower figure which is unchanged at -1 from this figure -2 to give $-2-(-1)$, that is $-2+1$ which is -1 or bar-one as before. As can be seen, either method yields the correct answer.

Example 2.11

Divide 0.74 by 0.98.

Number	Log
0.74	$\bar{1}.8692$
0.98	$\bar{1}.9912$
0.7551	$\bar{1}.8780$

The reader should work through this problem to ensure an understanding of how the final logarithm and thus the answer (0.7551) is obtained.

Roots and powers

To obtain the value of any number raised to a power, find the logarithm of the number, multiply the logarithm by the power and determine the antilogarithm (see example 2.5).

To obtain the value of a root of a number find the logarithm of the number, divide by the number of the root required (2 for square, 3 for cube, 4 for fourth, etc.) and determine the antilogarithm.

Example 2.12

Determine the cube root of (a) 4.784, (b) 0.4784.

(a)

$$\log 4.784 = 0.6798$$

$$\log 4.784^{1/3} = \frac{1}{3} \log 4.784$$

$$= 0.2266$$

Thus

$$4.784^{1/3} = \text{antilog } 0.2266$$

$$= 1.685$$

(b)

$$\log 0.4784 = \bar{1}.6798$$

$$\log 0.4784^{1/3} = \frac{1}{3} \log 0.4784$$

$$= \frac{1}{3} \times \bar{1}.6798$$

Care must be taken here since the characteristic is negative and the mantissa positive. Further the characteristic is not exactly divisible by 3. In a case like this the characteristic is made divisible by 3 by converting it to $\bar{3}$, that is -3. In order that the value of the logarithm shall remain the same the opposite of what has been done to the characteristic must be done to the mantissa, that is since the characteristic $\bar{1}$ has been reduced by -2 to make it -3, the mantissa must be increased by $+2$. Thus

$$\bar{1}.6798 = -1 + 0.6798$$

$$= -3 + 2.6798$$

Therefore

$$\frac{1}{3} \times \bar{1}.6798 = -1 + 0.8932$$

(Actually, $1/3 \times 2.6798 = 0.893266$ with 6 recurring. This equals 0.8933 to four places of decimals.)

Thus

$$\frac{1}{3} \times \bar{1}.6798 = \bar{1}.8933$$

and

$$0.4784^{1/3} = \text{antilog } \bar{1}.8933$$

$$= 0.7821$$

Example 2.13

Determine $0.345^{2/3}$

$0.345^{2/3}$ means the cube (third) root of the square of 0.345.

$$\log 0.345 \quad = \bar{1}.5378$$

$$\log 0.345^2 \; = 2 \times \bar{1}.5378$$

$$= \bar{1}.0756$$

Note the characteristic is $2 \times (-1) + 1$ carried over from 2×5.

$$\log 0.345^{2/3} = \frac{1}{3} \times \bar{1}.0756$$

$$= \frac{1}{3} \times (\bar{3} + 2.0756)$$

$$= \bar{1}.69186$$

$$= \bar{1}.6919 \text{ to four places of decimals}$$

Thus

$$0.345^{2/3} = 0.4919$$

from tables of antilogarithms.

The following examples are more difficult. They should be studied with care.

Example 2.14

Determine $(0.56)^{0.32}$

That is 0.56 raised to the power 0.32. This means 0.56 raised to the power 32/100 or the hundredth root of 0.56 multiplied by itself 31 times.

$$\log 0.56 \quad = \bar{1}.7482$$

$$\log (0.56)^{0.32} = 0.32 \times \bar{1}.7482$$

To avoid error it is advisable to convert $\bar{1}.7482$ which is a number containing a negative characteristic and positive mantissa into a wholly negative number.

$$\bar{1}.7482 \text{ means } -1 + 0.7482$$

that is

$$-0.2518$$

(take 0.7482 from 1 and put the result as a negative number)

Thus

$$\log (0.56)^{0.32} = -(0.32 \times 0.2518)$$

The term in the bracket may be determined either by ordinary (long) multiplication or by using logarithms. Remember however that this bracketed term is already a logarithm and will require conversion once determined.

$$\log 0.32 \qquad\qquad = \bar{1}.5051$$

$$\log 0.2518 \qquad\quad = \bar{1}.4011$$

$$\log (0.32 \times 0.2518) = \bar{1}.5051 + \bar{1}.4011$$

$$= \bar{2}.9062$$

thus

$$0.32 \times 0.2518 \quad = \text{antilog } \bar{2}.9062$$
$$= 0.08058$$
$$-(0.32 \times 0.2518) \quad = -0.08058$$

and from above

$$\log (0.56)^{0.32} \quad = -0.08058$$

but this is a wholly negative number and cannot be antilogged. It must be converted to a negative characteristic and a positive mantissa.

Now

$$-0.08058 = -1 + 0.91942$$

(To get 0.091942, subtract 0.08058 from 1.)

$$= \bar{1}.9194 \text{ to four places of decimals}$$

Thus

$$(0.56)^{0.32} = \text{antilog } \bar{1}.9194$$
$$= 0.8307$$

The next example is given without explanation.

Example 2.15

Evaluate 0.37 raised to the power 0.87.

$$\log 0.37 \quad = \bar{1} \ .5682$$
$$\log 0.37^{0.87} = 0.87 \times \bar{1}.5682$$
$$= 0.87 \times (-1 + 0.5682)$$
$$= -0.87 \times 0.4318$$

Number	Log
0.87	$\bar{1}$.9395
0.4318	$\bar{1}$.6353
0.3757	$\bar{1}$.5748

$$\log 0.37^{0.87} = -0.3757$$
$$= \bar{1}.6243$$

Therefore

$$0.37^{0.87} \quad = 0.4210$$

Exercise 2.2

Evaluate the following using logarithms

(1) 42.37×57.96

(7) $\dfrac{0.34 \times 0.73}{0.719}$

(2) $42.37 \div 5.796$

(8) 0.34×2.73^2

(3) $(73.45 \times 17.64)^{1/2}$

(9) $(0.197 \times 0.37)^{1/5}$

(4) $2.65 \times 0.78 \div 0.531$

(10) $0.197^{0.34}$

(5) $(523.4 \times 56.7)^{2/3}$

(11) $0.437^{0.25}$

(6) 0.34×0.73

(12) $\dfrac{18.71^{1/2} \times 0.356^{1/3}}{17.89^{1/4}}$

ROOTS AND RECIPROCALS FROM TABLES

Roots and reciprocals may easily be found using logarithms. However for convenience tables of these are often available; they are straightforward to read and are read in much the same way as logarithms. Care must be taken when reading square roots since there are two sets of tables with the same order of figures, that is, for example, one set contains 8.5, the other 85. Provided that one is careful to select the right table and to check the answer by estimation, as shown below, error should not ensue.

Example 2.16

Find the square root of the following from tables
    (a) 8.52   (b) 85.2   (c) 852   (d) 8520   (e) 0.852

(a) Find the tables headed 'square roots from 1 to 10'. Find 8.5 in far left-hand column, move along the line to column headed 2. Read off 2.919.

(b) Find the tables headed 'square roots from 10 to 100'. Find 85 in far left-hand column, move along the line to column headed 2. Read off 9.23.

(c) The order of the figures in the square root of 852 may be read off from tables. The question is which tables and where does the decimal point go? The technique is to write 852 containing a decimal point and using an *even* power of 10 as multiplier. The reason for this is shown below.

$$852 \quad = 8.52 \times 10^2$$
$$852^{1/2} = (8.52 \times 10^2)^{1/2}$$
$$= 8.52^{1/2} \times 10$$

that is

(square root of 8.52) × 10

Thus

$$852^{1/2} = 2.919 \times 10$$
$$= 29.19$$

This is a reasonable answer since the square of the next whole number (30) is of the same order as 852 (actually $30^2 = 900$).

(d)

$$8520 \quad = 85.2 \times 10^2$$

therefore

$$8520^{1/2} = 85.2^{1/2} \times 10$$
$$= 9.23 \times 10$$
$$= 92.3$$

(Again the answer is reasonable since $90^2 = 8100$.)

(e)

$$0.852 \quad = 85.2 \times 10^{-2}$$

therefore

$$0.852^{1/2} = (85.2 \times 10^{-2})^{1/2}$$
$$= 85.2^{1/2} \times 10^{-1}$$
$$= \frac{9.23}{10}$$
$$= 0.923$$

(This answer is of the right order since $0.9^2 = 0.81$.)

The reason for the even power of 10 is that when raising the multiplier to the power 1/2, that is finding its square root, the resultant power will be an integer and therefore easier to handle.

Example 2.17

Find the reciprocal of (a) 3.924, (b) 39.24, (c) 3924, (d) 0.3924.

(a) In the reciprocal tables 'reciprocals of numbers 1 to 10' find 3.9 in the left-hand column, move along the line to the column headed 2. Read off (but note this is not yet the answer) 2551. Continue along the line to the next set of columns, stop at the column headed 4. Read off difference 3. *Subtract* from 0.2551 to give 0.2548. Thus

$$\frac{1}{3.924} = 0.2548$$

The same tables may be used for the remaining parts of the problem but care must be taken when determining the position of the decimal point.

(b) The reciprocal of 39.24 will have the same figures in the same order as the reciprocal of 3.924, that is 2548, but the decimal point will move, since

$$\frac{1}{3.924} = 0.2548$$

$$\frac{1}{39.24} = 0.02548$$

that is since the denominator has increased ten-fold the answer will be 1/10 of the previous answer.

(c) Similarly

$$\frac{1}{3924} = 0.0002548$$

(d) And

$$\frac{1}{0.3924} = 2.548$$

Since 3924 is 1000 × 3.924 the answer is $\frac{1}{1000}$ of 0.2548.

Since 0.3924 is $\frac{1}{10}$ × 3.924 the answer is 10 × 0.2548.

In general, use the 1 to 10 tables of reciprocals and adjust the position of the point.

Exercise 2.3

Use tables to find the following

(1) $3.982^{1/2}$ (5) $1/37.56$ (9) $0.3756^{-1/2}$

(2) $398.2^{1/2}$ (6) $1/3.756$ (10) $374.2^{-1/2}$

(3) $0.3982^{1/2}$ (7) 0.3756^{-1} (11) $0.087^{-1/2}$

(4) $0.03982^{1/2}$ (8) 0.03756^{-1} (12) $87.43^{-1/2}$

THE SLIDE RULE

The slide rule is a most useful aid to calculations and when used proficiently reduces considerably the time required. The results obtained are not generally as accurate as those produced using logarithms but are adequate for most engineering purposes.

The slide rule has three parts, a fixed part called the *stock*, a sliding part called the *slide*—both of which have scales marked on them—and a third, transparent, piece marked with a fine line used for aligning scale markings on the other parts. The third part is called the *cursor* and is also movable along the stock. The fine line on the cursor is called the *cursor line,* see figure 2.1

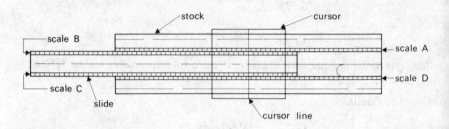

Figure 2.1   Basic elements of the slide rule

The slide rule uses the principle of logarithms but makes unnecessary the process of finding the logarithms and antilogarithms of numbers. Scales C and D shown in the figure are marked with numbers from 1 to 10 such that the distance between the mark for a particular number and the mark for 1 represents the logarithm of that number. Thus since the logarithm of 5 for example is 0.699 then the distance between the 1 mark and the 5 mark is 0.699 of the total scale length. The total scale length, representing 1—the logarithm of 10—is the distance between the 1 mark and the 10 mark. Similarly the distance between the 1 mark and the 3 mark is 0.4771 of the total scale length (since log 3 is 0.4771); the distance between the 1 mark and the 4 mark is 0.6021 of the total scale length (since log 4 is 0.6021); and so on.

Example 2.18

The C and D scales of a slide rule marked from 1 to 10 have a length of 250 mm. Determine the distance between the 4 mark and the 7.5 mark.

Distance between 4 mark and 1 mark is 0.6021 of 250 mm (since log 4 = 0.6021). Distance between 7.5 mark and 1 mark is 0.8751 of 250 mm (since log 7.5 = 0.8751). Thus distance between 4 mark and 7.5 mark equals

$$(0.8751-0.6021) \text{ of } 250 \text{ mm}$$

that is

$$0.2730 \times 250 \text{ mm}$$

which equals 68.25 mm.

Using the slide rule

The method of use for multiplication and division, which is standard for all slide rules, is considered in detail below. Many other calculations are possible but in most of these the method depends on the make of rule and the reader is referred to the instruction leaflet for the particular rule.

One general point is to note that all markings on the scales are not numbered because of lack of space and their value must be inferred from the nearest numbered marks. The distance between numbered marks is divided into as many parts as the available rule length allows. (It will be noted that because of the logarithmic scale the separation between the 1 mark and the 2 mark is much greater than, say, the separation between the 8 mark and the 9 mark.) Figure 2.2 shows a few examples of reading between numbers.

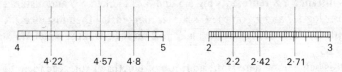

Figure 2.2   Reading scales between numbers

Multiplication

Example 2.19
Multiply 5.5 by 1.7.

Set the 1 mark on scale C to the 5.5 mark on scale D.
Slide the cursor to the 1.7 mark on scale C.
Read off the number on scale D which is in line with the 1.7 mark on scale C. This number is 9.35 and is the answer. To understand why this is so examine figure 2.3.

The distance between the 1.7 mark on scale C and the 1 mark on scale D is equal to the distance between the 5.5 mark on scale D and the 1 mark on scale D added to the distance between the 1.7 mark on scale C and the 1 mark on scale C. That is using the letters shown in the diagram

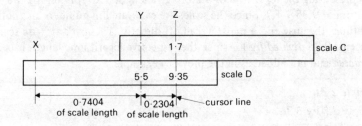

Figure 2.3   Example 2.19

distance ZX = distance YX + distance ZY

but

distance YX = log 5.5 × scale length

and

distance ZY = log 1.7 × scale length

therefore

distance ZX = (log 5.5 × scale length) + (log 1.7 × scale length)

= (log 5.5 + log 1.7) × scale length

= [log (5.5 × 1.7)] × scale length

Thus as distance YX represents log 5.5 and Y is marked 5.5 and distance ZY represents log 1.7 and Z (on the C scale) is marked 1.7 then distance ZX represents log (5.5 × 1.7) and the mark at Z on scale D must equal 5.5 × 1.7, that is 9.35.

What is being done here is the addition of lengths of rule, each length being proportional to the logarithm of a number, to give a total length determined by the logarithm of the product of the numbers. By suitably marking the scales in numbers (while making the *lengths* depend on logarithms) the need for finding logarithms and antilogarithms is made unnecessary and the answer may be read off directly.

Division

Division is the reverse of multiplication and as such the opposite process is carried out with the slide rule.

Example 2.20

Divide 9.35 by 1.7.

Using the cursor set 1.7 on scale C to lie immediately above 9.35 on scale D. The mark on scale D lying below the 1 mark on scale C is 9.35 divided by 1.7. The answer is 5.5. See figure 2.3 again.

Here length ZY representing the logarithm of 1.7 is *subtracted* from length ZX representing the logarithm of 9.35 to give length YX representing the logarithm of 9.35 ÷ 1.7. Since the scales are calibrated in numbers and not logarithms, the answer 5.5 may be read off directly. The mark at Y on scale D represents 9.35 *divided by* 1.7 since the respective logarithmic length is being *subtracted* and not added as in the previous example.

Example 2.21

Multiply 5.5 by 3.78.

Set 1 mark (C scale) to 5.5 mark (D scale). It is seen that 3.78 mark (C scale) lies beyond the end of the D scale so the corresponding mark on the D scale cannot be read off.

Instead set 10 mark (C scale) to 5.5 mark (D scale). Using the cursor read off the number of the mark on the D scale lying immediately below the 3.78 mark on the C scale. This is 2.08 (check carefully).

Now 2.08 clearly cannot be the right answer since 5 x 3 is 15 and thus 5.5 x 3.78 must be larger than 15. The answer is therefore 20.8.

From this example we see that the slide rule gives the figures of an answer in the correct order but unlike logarithms does not place the decimal point.

This must be done by estimation, one particularly useful aid being to use standard form (see chapter 1). This is further explained in example 2.23.

Example 2.22
Divide 20.8 by 3.78.

Set 3.78 (C scale) immediately above 2.08 (D scale). 1 on the C scale is beyond the end of the D scale, so read the D scale opposite the 10 on the C scale. The figures of the answer are 5.5 and by estimation the answer is in fact 5.5 (there are five fours in 20 thus there will be slightly more than five times 3.78 in 20.8).

Example 2.23
Evaluate $\dfrac{23.4 \times 56.7}{13.9}$

Set 10 on C scale to 2.34 on D scale. Move cursor to 5.67 on C scale (this is not marked so an estimate of where 5.67 lies must be made). Leave cursor and move slide until 1.39 on C scale is aligned with cursor line. Read D scale opposite 10 on C scale. Figures are 9.55. The question is where does the decimal point lie? What the slide rule has actually calculated for us is

$$\frac{2.34 \times 5.67}{1.39}$$

which would have the same figures in the same order as the required answer. The magnitude of the answer would however be different.
Write

$$\frac{23.4 \times 56.7}{13.9}$$

as

$$\frac{2.34 \times 10 \times 5.67 \times 10}{1.39 \times 10}$$

that is

$$\frac{2.34 \times 5.67}{1.39} \times 10$$

that is slide rule answer x 10, so the answer is 95.5.

Example 2.24

Evaluate $\dfrac{963 \times 25.7 \times 14.8}{13.2 \times 351}$

Set 10 (scale C) to 9.63 (scale D). Move cursor to 2.57 (scale C). Leave cursor. Move 1 (scale C) to line up with cursor mark. Move cursor to 1.48 (scale C). Leave cursor. Align 1.32 (scale C) with cursor line. Move cursor to 1 (scale C). Leave cursor. Align 3.51 (scale C) with cursor line. Read scale D opposite 10 on scale C. Number is 7.9.

Rewrite the problem as

$$\frac{9.63 \times 10 \times 2.57 \times 10 \times 1.48 \times 10}{1.32 \times 10 \times 3.51 \times 10}$$

that is

$$\frac{9.63 \times 2.57 \times 1.48}{1.32 \times 3.51} \times 10$$

which equals

$$7.9 \times 10$$

The answer is 79.

The reader is advised to obtain as much practice as possible with problems, particularly of the kind shown in the last example. An exercise is given below. The reader is also reminded once more to study the instruction leaflet with the slide rule and practice the processes involved in raising the powers and finding roots (the extent of the calculations which may be performed depend on the slide rule).

Exercise 2.4

Use a slide rule to calculate the following

(1) 12.74×13.65

(2) $139 \div 53.2$

(3) $\dfrac{1.35 \times 17}{7.8}$

(4) $\dfrac{18.9 \times 3.5}{7.2 \times 5}$

(5) $\left(\dfrac{18.3 \times 17.2}{5.6}\right)^2$

(6) $1.35^3 \times 17.4^2$

(7) $\left(\dfrac{125 \times 17.5}{32.4}\right)^4$

(8) $\left(\dfrac{19.73}{5.74}\right)^5$

(9) $\dfrac{17.8^2 \times 14.73}{15.6^2}$

(10) $\dfrac{345 \times 15.6}{4.2 \times 19.2 \times 1.7}$

Note when raising to a power multiply the number by itself the appropriate number of times.

3 Algebra

If we wish to refer to a quantity in engineering such as mass, length, time, voltage, current, etc., without giving it a particular numerical value, we may use a symbol or letter to indicate the quantity. For example instead of writing the word 'mass' we could use the letter m, or for 'time' the letter t. The use of such letters saves a great deal of time and energy and greatly helps the engineer's task of determining how one quantity affects another. The branch of mathematics using letters and symbols in this way is called *algebra*.

One of the basic relationships between physical quantities is that power is equal to the rate of using energy, that is power equals energy divided by time. Instead of continually writing the words 'power', 'energy' and 'time' we could refer to these quantities using the letters P, E and t. Thus we could then say

$$P = \frac{E}{t}$$

This is an *algebraic equation* and is true for all values of P, E and t provided of course that they are measured in units from the same system. Before we examine such equations and their manipulation we must first consider the basic rules of algebra. Remember throughout the next few pages that letters such as a, b, c, or x, y, z, would actually represent quantities in practice. We shall not necessarily say what they represent as we examine the basic rules.

BASIC CONSIDERATIONS

In algebra the letters assigned to quantities are usually referred to as *variables* since they may have any numerical value as determined by the value of the quantity for a particular circumstance. Any letter or symbol may be used to represent a variable quantity, the most common when examining basic rules

71

being x, y, a, b, c. These will be the ones most used in the next few pages; remember however that the rules apply to any variable.

An algebraic term such as $3x$ or $4x$ means 3 multiplied by x or 4 multiplied by x
so that
$$3x = 3 \times x = x + x + x$$
and
$$4x = 4 \times x = x + x + x + x$$

The number preceding the variable (3 or 4 in the above examples) is called the *coefficient* of the variable. The coefficient of x (or of a or b) is obviously 1. The coefficient need not be a whole number; $x/4$, for example, has the coefficient $1/4$ and means one-quarter of x.

The algebraic term x^2 means x multiplied by itself once, x^3 means x multiplied by itself twice, and so on. The rules of powers discussed in chapter 1 (in which they applied to raising numbers to various powers) apply equally when dealing with algebraic quantities.

Brackets may be used in algebraic expressions in the same way as in arithmetic and whatever process is indicated by whatever lies outside the bracket applies equally to all terms within the bracket. The rules summarised by the word BODMAS discussed earlier apply equally to algebraic expressions and such expressions can be factorised to give other simpler expressions which when multiplied together yield the original.

In algebra we must expect to meet negative quantities. This is not entirely new. As explained earlier the term 'positive' merely means the opposite of negative and whatever process or characteristics implied by one sign, the opposite is implied by the other. Thus in chapter 1 a positive power indicated a fraction numerator, a negative power indicated a denominator. In algebra, where a letter represents a variable quantity, positive and negative signs can have a variety of meanings. For instance $+1$ (usually written 1 with the $+$ sign omitted) may mean a length measured in a certain direction; -1 would therefore mean a length measured in the opposite direction. Similarly, P could mean power delivered from a supply to a load in which case $-P$ would indicate the load returning the power to the supply. (This happens in some electrical circuits.)

The rules that apply when performing arithmetical operations (adding, subtracting, etc.) on positive and negative numbers were explained in chapter 1 using the laws of powers. However these rules apply equally when performing arithmetical operations on algebraic quantities. The rules will be reviewed as necessary during the following detailed examination.

Addition

If one algebraic quantity is to be added to another the coefficients may be added provided that the variable or variables are the same in each case. They may not be added if the variables are different.

For example $3x + 4x = 7x$, but $3p + 4q$ cannot be further reduced. Similarly $(-3x) + (-4x) = -7x$. This is the addition of negative quantities. Note the use of brackets and the fact that a positive sign outside the bracket leaves the sign (or signs) within the bracket unchanged. The last example could equally be written

$$-3x - 4x = -7x$$

Examples of addition of quantities having different signs are

$$-3x + 4x = x$$
$$3x - 4x = -x$$

In the first of these the negative $3x$ cancels $3x$ of the positive $4x$ leaving x. In the second example the positive $3x$ cancels $-3x$ of the negative $4x$ leaving $-x$. (*Note* that both of these examples could be considered a subtraction of one positive quantity from another positive quantity. The result is of course the same however the problem is considered.)

Subtraction

If one algebraic quantity is to be subtracted from another the coefficients may be subtracted provided that the variable or variables are the same in each case. This is not so if the variables are different. For example $4x - 3x = x$, but $4p - 3q$ cannot be further reduced. (*Note* that $4x - 3x$ could be considered as an algebraic addition of a positive quantity to a negative quantity. The rule and the result are the same.)

Similarly

$$4x - (-3x) = 7x$$

Note the use of brackets and also that a negative sign outside a bracket changes the signs inside.
Similarly

$$-4x - (-3x)$$
$$= -4x + 3x$$
$$= -x$$

($-4x + 3x$ may be considered as an algebraic addition of a negative quantity to a positive quantity. The rule and the result are the same.)

Study the following examples before continuing with multiplication and division.

Example 3.1

Simplify (a) $4x + 3y - 7x - 4y + 6x - 2y$
         (b) $3x - (-4x) + 7(x-y) + 3y$
         (c) $9a - 8b + 7(6a - 4b)$
         (d) $12a + 5x - 7x + 10a - 3x$

(a) Coefficients of x are $4 - 7 + 6$ which equals 3
and of y are $-7 -4 -2$ which equals -13.
The answer is thus $3x - 13y$.

(b) Rewrite before summing coefficients (brackets before addition and subtraction).

$$3x - (-4x) + 7(x-y) + 3y = 3x + 4x + 7x - 7y + 3y$$

(*Note* application of sign rule.)

Coefficients of x are $3 + 4 + 7$, that is 14, and of y are $-7 + 3$, that is -4; the answer is $14x - 4y$.

(c) $9a - 8b + 7(6a - 4b) = 9a - 8b + 42a - 28b$
$$= 51a - 36b$$

(d) $12a + 5x - 7x + 10a - 3x = 22a - 5x$

Multiplication

Multiplication of algebraic quantities is straightforward, the variables in each term being multiplied following one another in the multiple, the coefficient of the multiple being the product of the coefficients of the terms being multiplied. Due regard must be paid to the rules regarding signs of quantities which are

product of like signs yields resultant positive
product of unlike signs yields resultant negative

thus $3a \times 3b = 9ab$ and $-3a \times -3b = 9ab$ but $-3a \times 3b = -9ab$.

Example 3.2

(a) Simplify $3a \times 3b \times 3c$

The answer is $27abc$ (meaning 27 times a times b times c).

(b) Simplify $3ab(ab + 2cd + b)$

Note the use of brackets; all terms within the bracket must be multiplied by the $3ab$ term outside. Thus the answer is

$$3a^2b^2 + 6abcd + 3ab^2$$

where $a^2 = a \times a$ and $b^2 = b \times b$.

When multiple brackets are used, simplify the inner ones first, working out to the outer ones.

Example 3.3
Simplify $3a[4a - 2b(3a + 3b)]$

This equals

$$3a(4a - 6ab - 6b^2)$$

(*Note* the product of unlike signs.) And this equals

$$12a^2 - 18a^2b - 18ab^2$$

Example 3.4
Simplify $4a[3b(a-b) + 2a(a+b)]$

This equals

$$4a(3ab - 3b^2 + 2a^2 + 2ab)$$
$$= 4a(5ab - 3b^2 + 2a^2)$$

(*Note* addition of like quantities $3ab + 2ab$ to equal $5ab$.)

$$= 20a^2b - 12ab^2 + 8a^3$$

When multiplying two or more sets of bracketed quantities every term in one bracketed expression must be multiplied by every term in the other.

Example 3.5
Simplify $(a + b)(a + b)$

$$(a + b)(a + b) = a(a + b) + b(a + b)$$
$$= a^2 + ab + ab + b^2$$
$$= a^2 + 2ab + b^2$$

Notice that $(a+b)(a+b)$ is in fact $(a+b)^2$ so that this example gives us a general rule for squaring such expressions containing two terms. The rule is—square the first term, square the second, multiply both terms together and multiply the product by two; the three new terms obtained added together equal the square of the original expression.

Thus for example

$$(b + c)^2 = b^2 + 2bc + c^2$$

and

$$(x + y)^2 = x^2 + 2xy + y^2$$

Example 3.6

Simplify $(a^2 + 3ab + b^2)(a - b)$

$$(a^2 + 3ab + b^2)(a-b) = a(a^2 + 3ab + b^2) - b(a^2 + 3ab + b^2)$$
$$= a^3 + 3a^2b + ab^2 - a^2b - 3ab^2 - b^3$$
$$= a^3 + 2a^2b - 2ab^2 - b^3$$

Note that

$$3a^2b - a^2b = 2a^2b$$

and

$$ab^2 - 3ab^2 = -2ab^2$$

The opposite process of multiplication, that is determining the terms which when multiplied together give a particular expression is called *factorisation*. Thus $a^3 + 2a^2b - 2ab^2 - b^3 = (a^2 + 3ab + b^2)(a - b)$ where $(a^2 + 3ab + b^2)$ and $(a - b)$ are *factors* of $a^3 + 2a^2b - 2ab^2 - b^3$. Similarly from example 3.5 $(a + b)$ is a factor of $a^2 + 2ab + b^2$.

Division

When dividing one algebraic quantity by another the variables are written in the appropriate fractional form, the coefficient of the answer being determined by dividing the coefficients of the original quantities. Simplification by cancellation of factors may be carried out on both coefficient and variable where this is possible. The rule of signs must be adhered to in all cases, this is

positive divided by positive is positive
positive divided by negative is negative
negative divided by negative is positive
negative divided by positive is negative.

This rule follows from that of multiplication.

For example

$$4a \div 3b \quad = \frac{4a}{3b}$$

$$4a \div -3b \quad = \frac{-4a}{3b}$$

$$-4a \div -3b = \frac{4a}{3b}$$

$$-4a \div +3b = \frac{-4a}{3b}$$

and showing simplification

$$4a \div 3a \quad = \frac{4a}{3a}$$

$$= \frac{4}{3} \quad \text{(dividing through by } a\text{)}$$

$$5ab \div -2a = \frac{-5ab}{2a}$$

$$= \frac{-5b}{2} \quad \text{(dividing through by } a\text{)}$$

More complex divisions may also be simplified using factorisation.

Example 3.7
Divide $12a^2 + 24ab + 12b^2$ by $a + b$

$$\frac{12a^2 + 24ab + 12b^2}{a+b} = \frac{12(a^2 + 2ab + b^2)}{a+b}$$

$$= \frac{12(a+b)(a+b)}{a+b} \quad \text{(from example 3.5)}$$

$$= 12(a+b)$$

Example 3.8
Divide $15xy + 25x + 5y$ by $5xy$

This equals

$$\frac{15xy + 25x + 5y}{5xy}$$

Divide $5xy$ into each term to give

$$\frac{15xy}{5xy} + \frac{25x}{5xy} + \frac{5y}{5xy}$$

$$= 3 + \frac{5}{y} + \frac{1}{x}$$

Exercise 3.1
Simplify the following

(a) $4ax(x+y)$

(b) $5a[3x + 2(1+x)]$

(c) $(x+y)(x-y)$

(d) $4xy + 6x - 2xy - 7y + x$

(e) $5xy - 3xy + x \div 2xy$

(f) $(a+b)(a^2 + 2ab + b^2) \div (a+b)$

(g) $abcd[a^2 + b^2(1-c) + 3ab] \div bd$

(h) $(x - 2y)(x + 3y) \div 4x$

(i) $(x^2 + 2xy + y^2 + xy + y^2) \div (x+y)$

(j) $\dfrac{4ab + 3cd - ab - c + cd}{abcd}$

ALGEBRAIC FRACTIONS

The rules of fractions discussed in chapter 1 apply equally to algebra.
Fractions are added or subtracted in the same manner as in arithmetic, that is
by finding the lowest common denominator; multiplication or division of
fractions is only an extension of the methods used in the preceding examples.
Care must be taken to apply the rules regarding signs at all times.

Example 3.9

Express the following as a single fraction

(a) $\dfrac{5}{3}a + \dfrac{3}{2}b + \dfrac{1}{2}a + \dfrac{2}{3}b$ (d) $\dfrac{4(a+b)}{a^2 b} + \dfrac{5(a-b)}{ab^2}$

(b) $\dfrac{5}{ab} + \dfrac{3}{a} + \dfrac{7}{b}$ (e) $\dfrac{1}{x} - \dfrac{3}{5x}$

(c) $\dfrac{4a}{a+b} + \dfrac{5b}{a-b}$

(a) In this example bear in mind that only like terms may be added.
Thus

$$\frac{5}{3}a + \frac{3}{2}b + \frac{1}{2}a + \frac{2}{3}b = \left(\frac{5}{3} + \frac{1}{2}\right) a + \left(\frac{3}{2} + \frac{2}{3}\right) b$$

(Note the use of brackets.)

$$= \left(\frac{10+3}{6}\right) a + \left(\frac{9+4}{6}\right) b$$

$$= \frac{13a}{6} + \frac{13b}{6}$$

$$= \frac{13}{6}(a+b)$$

(b) The lowest common denominator for $5/ab + 3/a + 7/b$ is ab. Thus we
wish to put ab as the denominator in each case and shall therefore have to adjust
the numerator accordingly.

To write $3/a$ with a denominator of ab means multiplying the original
denominator a by b; to ensure the value of $3/a$ remains unchanged the numerator
must also be multiplied by b. So that

$$\frac{3}{a} = \frac{3b}{ab}$$

Similarly

$$\frac{7}{b} = \frac{7a}{ab}$$

and

$$\frac{5}{ab} + \frac{3}{a} + \frac{7}{b} = \frac{5}{ab} + \frac{3b}{ab} + \frac{7a}{ab}$$

$$= \frac{5 + 3b + 7a}{ab}$$

(c) The lowest common denominator here is the product of the two, that is $(a + b)(a - b)$, and adjusting the numerators as shown in the previous example we have

$$\frac{4a}{a+b} + \frac{5b}{a-b} = \frac{4a(a-b) + 5b(a+b)}{(a+b)(a-b)}$$

$$= \frac{4a^2 - 4ab + 5ab + 5b^2}{a^2 + ab - ab - b^2}$$

$$= \frac{4a^2 + ab + 5b^2}{a^2 - b^2}$$

Note in this example the addition of like quantities (of opposite signs) $-4ab + 5ab$ to give ab.

The denominator $(a + b)(a - b)$ multiplies out to $(a^2 - b^2)$. Such an expression, called the *difference of two squares*, can always be factorised in this way, that is as

$$a^2 - b^2 = (a + b)(a - b)$$

so

$$c^2 - d^2 = (c + d)(c - d)$$

and

$$x^2 - y^2 = (x + y)(x - y)$$

and so on. This is a useful fact to remember for simplification purposes in some problems.

(d)

$$\frac{4(a+b)}{a^2 b} + \frac{5(a-b)}{ab^2} = \frac{4b(a+b) + 5a(a-b)}{a^2 b^2}$$

$$= \frac{4ab + 4b^2 + 5a^2 - 5ab}{a^2 b^2}$$

$$= \frac{5a^2 - ab + 4b^2}{a^2 b^2}$$

Note in this example the lowest common denominator is not the product of the denominators (which would be $a^2 b \times ab^2$, that is $a^3 b^3$) but is $a^2 b^2$. This can be determined by looking at the separate denominators and realising that the common denominator must first be of the form 'power of $a \times$ power of b'; second it must have a^2 in it to accommodate the a^2 in $a^2 b$, and third it must have b^2 in it to accommodate the b^2 in ab^2. To ensure that individual fractions do not change their value when the denominator is changed to a^2b^2, $4(a + b)/a^2b$ must be multiplied through by b and $5(a - b)/ab^2$ must be multiplied through by a.

(e) Common denominator is $5x$ which contains both x and $5x$. Thus

$$\frac{1}{x} - \frac{3}{5x} = \frac{5}{5x} - \frac{3}{5x}$$

$$= \frac{5 - 3}{5x}$$

$$= \frac{2}{5x}$$

Exercise 3.2

Express as a single fraction

(a) $\dfrac{1}{x} + \dfrac{1}{y}$

(b) $\dfrac{2}{xy} + \dfrac{3}{x} + \dfrac{4}{y}$

(c) $\dfrac{1}{a - b} + \dfrac{1}{a + b}$

(d) $\dfrac{4}{a} + \dfrac{3}{b} - \dfrac{2}{c}$

(e) $\dfrac{1}{x + y} + \dfrac{5x}{x(x + y)} + \dfrac{7y}{y}$

(f) $\dfrac{8 + x}{x + y} - \dfrac{4 + y}{x - y}$

(g) $\dfrac{3a + b}{ab} - \dfrac{4ab}{a + b}$

POWERS (INDICES)

The rules involved when raising a number to a power were discussed in some detail in chapter 1. These rules apply in exactly the same way to algebraic quantities and because of the importance and wide application of the process in mathematics generally they will be re-examined below. One point to note before we begin is that another name for power is *index,* the plural of which is *indices.* Thus in the term a^5, for example, a is the base (as previously defined) and 5 is the index.

Meaning of powers

a^3 means $a \times a \times a$

a^4 means $a \times a \times a \times a$

and in general raising any algebraic quantity or expression to a power means multiplying the quantity or expression by itself a number of times equal to one less than the power. When multiplying quantities raised to a power the powers are *added* provided the base is the same.

For example
$$a^5 \times a^4 = a^9$$
and
$$(a + b)^2 \times (a + b)^3 = (a + b)^5$$

When dividing such quantities the index of the denominator is subtracted from the index of the numerator (again, provided the base is the same). Thus
$$a^5 \div a^4 = a$$
and
$$(x + y)^4 \div (x + y)^2 = (x + y)^2$$

When raising to powers in succession the indices are multiplied. Thus
$$(x^5)^4 = x^{20}$$
and
$$[(a - b)^2]^3 = (a - b)^6$$
and so on.

One common error occurs when manipulating expressions such as $a^5 + a^5$. This equals $2a^5$ *not* a^{10}. For the simplified version to be a^{10}, the plus sign shown must be a multiplication sign, that is $a^5 \times a^5$ to give a^{5+5}.

Example 3.8

Simplify the following

(a) $4x^3 y^2 (3xy + 5xy)^2 \div 8x^2 y^2$

(b) $(a + b)^2 \times (a + b)^2$

(c) $[(x^2 - y^2)(x^2 + y^2)]^2 \div xy$

(a) First clear the bracket
$$(3xy + 5xy)^2 = (8xy)^2 \text{ [addition of like quantities]}$$
$$= 64x^2 y^2$$

(Notice that the power applies to all numbers and variables.)
Thus
$$4x^3 y^2 (3xy + 5xy)^2 = 4x^3 y^2 \times 64x^2 y^2$$
$$= 256x^5 y^4 \text{ (addition of powers of common bases)}$$

Dividing by $8x^2 y^2$ gives
$$\frac{256x^5 y^4}{8x^2 y^2}$$
$$32x^3 y^2 \text{ (subtraction of powers of common base)}$$

(b)
$$(a + b)^2 \times (a + b)^2 = (a + b)^4$$
$$= (a + b)(a + b)(a + b)(a + b)$$
$$= (a^2 + 2ab + b^2)(a^2 + 2ab + b^2)$$

(Squaring—see example 3.5.)

Now multiply every term in the second bracket by every term in the first

$$\text{second bracket} \times a^2 \quad = a^4 + 2a^3b + a^2b^2$$
$$\text{second bracket} \times 2ab = 2a^3b + 4a^2b^2 + 2ab^3$$
$$\text{second bracket} \times b^2 \quad = a^2b^2 + 2ab^3 + b^4$$

Thus the whole expression is

$$a^4 + 2a^3b + a^2b^2 + 2a^3b + 4a^2b^2 + 2ab^3 + a^2b^2 + 2ab^3 + b^4$$

Adding like quantities gives

$$a^4 + 4a^3b + 5a^2b^2 + 4ab^3 + b^4$$

(since $2a^3b + 2a^3b = 4a^3b$, $2ab^3 + 2ab^3 = 4ab^3$ and $a^2b^2 + 4a^2b^2 = 5a^2b^2$).

(c) The contents of the square bracket represent a difference of two squares (see example 3.9c) and thus

$$(x^2 - y^2)(x^2 + y^2) = x^4 - y^4$$

The problem simplifies to

$$(x^4 - y^4)^2 \div xy$$

Now

$$(x^4 - y^4)^2 = x^8 - 2x^4y^4 + y^8$$

(Square of first term, that is $(x^4)^2$, $+ 2 \times$ product of $(x^4)(y^4)$ + square of last term, that is $(y^4)^2$, see example 3.5.)
Thus the problem becomes

$$\frac{x^8 - 2x^4y^4 + y^8}{xy}$$

which can be written

$$\frac{x^7}{y} - 2x^3y^3 + \frac{y^7}{x}$$

(Either from may be used. One is not necessarily simpler than the other—it depends on the use to which the expression is to be put.)

Exercise 3.3

Simplify the following leaving the answers with positive powers

(a) $[(3x + y)^2 + y]^2$

(b) $(m^3n^2 - 1)^2 \div 2mn(m^5n^4)$

(c) $\dfrac{a^{-4}b^{-3}c^2 \times a^{-2}b^{-2}c}{abc}$

(d) $(a^2 + b)^2(a^2 - b)^2 \div (a^4 - b^2)$

(e) $[(m^2)^3 \times (n^3)^2]^{1/6}$

(f) $(abc + 3abc - 2abc + abd - 5abd)^2$

(g) $(xy^4 + x^2y^3 + x^3y^2 + x^4y) \div x^5y^5$

(h) $[(a^2 + b^2) \times (a^2 + b^2) \times (ab)^{-1}]^{-1}$

4 Formulae and Equations

In the introduction to algebra in chapter 3 it was stated that algebra is a means of referring to physical quantities using symbols instead of writing the name of the quantity in full. Thus instead of writing the basic relationship between voltage, current and resistance, for example, as

$$\frac{\text{voltage}}{\text{current}} = \text{resistance}$$

we might write

$$\frac{V}{I} = R$$

where

V represents voltage (measured in volts)
I represents current (measured in ampères)
R represents resistance (measured in ohms)

This relationship is called an *equation*. The expression V/I could be referred to as the *formula* for resistance. In this chapter we shall be further examining formulae (note the plural) and equations, in particular looking at the process of *transposition* when it is desired to change the *subject* of a formula and also at the solution of equations, that is finding the value of a variable (the *unknown*) under circumstances where all other determining factors are known.

TRANSPOSITION

In the formula $R = V/I$ given above, the resistance R is the *subject* of the formula since its value is given in terms of the values of voltage V and current I at any particular time.

For example, if $V = 10$ volts and $I = 5$ ampères then R is $10/5$, that is 2 ohms.

Arranged in this way it is easier and more convenient to find R for all the different values that V and I may have. However, in many circumstances the voltage and resistance may be known, in which case it may be required to find the value of the current. The formula now required is of the form in which current I lies on the left-hand side with the variables V and R, appropriately arranged, on the right-hand side. By 'appropriately arranged' we mean that they must be arranged in a way which does not alter in any way the scientific truth of the statement that resistance is equal to voltage divided by current. This rearrangement is called *transposition* of the formula—in this case making I the subject. Transposition must be carefully handled since any error will result in making a statement which is not true. In engineering the use of an untrue mathematical statement could at best lead to the loss of expensive equipment or components, and at worst the loss of human life. It is therefore essential never to make changes in an equation without ensuring that the original truth is unaltered.

A formula or equation giving the relationship between one variable and other variables may be likened to a balance in which masses are compared when the masses are equal. Anything which is done to one side of the balance *must* be done to the other or the state of balance is changed. With an equation or formula this would mean that the original equality (implied by the sign =) is no longer valid if one side of the equation is changed differently to the other.

To return to the formula $R = V/I$. To make I the subject multiply both sides by I giving

$$IR = \frac{VI}{I}$$

thus

$$IR = V$$

(since I divided by I is unity).

Now divide both sides by R

$$\frac{IR}{R} = \frac{V}{R}$$

and so

$$I = \frac{V}{R}$$

To make V the subject

$$R = \frac{V}{L}$$

multiply both sides by I as before

$$IR = \frac{VI}{I}$$

that is

$$V = IR$$

(Note that the sides may be interchanged from left to right provided that they are not altered in any way in so doing.)

Study the following examples carefully

Example 4.1

The relationship between electrical resistance R, resistivity ρ, conductor length l and conductor cross-sectional area A is given by

$$R = \rho \frac{l}{A}$$

Make the resistivity ρ the subject of the formula.

Multiply both sides by A

$$AR = \rho \frac{lA}{A}$$
$$= \rho l$$

Divide both sides by l

$$\frac{AR}{l} = \rho \frac{l}{l}$$
$$= \rho$$

thus

$$\rho = \frac{AR}{l}$$

that is

$$\text{resistivity} = \frac{\text{area} \times \text{resistance}}{\text{length}}$$

Example 4.2

The velocity of a moving body v after a time t spent accelerating with a constant acceleration a is given by

$$v = u + at$$

where u is the velocity of the body at the beginning of time t. Make t the subject of this formula.

Subtract u from both sides

$$v - u = u - u + at$$
$$= at$$

Divide both sides by a

$$\frac{v-u}{a} = \frac{at}{a}$$

$$= t$$

Thus

$$t = \frac{v-u}{a}$$

that is

$$\text{time} = \frac{\text{final velocity} - \text{initial velocity}}{\text{acceleration}}$$

From the above examples some basic rules of transposition can be seen. These are: first isolate the term containing the required subject on one side of the equation (in example 4.2 by subtracting u from both sides); second isolate the subject. If the subject is contained in the numerator of a fraction then divide through by any multiplier in the same numerator (dividing by l in example 4.1 and by a in example 4.2) and multiply through by the denominator of the fraction containing the subject (A in example 4.1, 'denominator' of unity in example 4.2 and thus multiplication is not necessary).

Example 4.3

When a conductor is heated the resistance changes. The resistance after heating R_1 in terms of the resistance at $0°C$ R_0, the temperature after heating T_1 and the temperature coefficient of resistance of the conductor α is given by

$$R_1 = R_0(1 + \alpha T_1)$$

Make α the subject of this formula

First we must isolate αT_1 then α. This is done as follows

$$R_1 = R_0(1 + \alpha T_1)$$

Divide both sides by R_0

$$\frac{R_1}{R_0} = \frac{R_0}{R_0}(1 + \alpha T_1)$$

that is

$$\frac{R_1}{R_0} = 1 + \alpha T_1$$

Subtract 1 from both sides

$$\frac{R_1}{R_0} - 1 = \alpha T_1$$

Divide both sides by T_1

$$\frac{1}{T_1}\left(\frac{R_1}{R_0} - 1\right) = \alpha$$

This makes α the subject. Note the use of brackets to show that all terms within are being divided by T_1 (or multiplied by $1/T_1$, which is the same thing).

The above equation may be written without brackets as follows

Write 1 in the left-hand side as R_0/R_0, that is

$$\frac{1}{T_1}\left(\frac{R_1}{R_0} - \frac{R_0}{R_0}\right) = \alpha$$

This gives us a subtraction of fractions having the same denominator in the bracket and thus we may write

$$\frac{1}{T_1}\left(\frac{R_1 - R_0}{R_0}\right) = \alpha$$

or

$$\frac{R_1 - R_0}{R_0 T_1} = \alpha$$

In the preceding examples the formulae were explained as part of the problem. In mathematical test papers and examinations this is not always the case. However it is not necessary to know the meaning of the formula to practise transposition.

Example 4.4

Make a the subject of $y = \dfrac{ax + b}{c}$

Multiply through by c

$$cy = ax + b$$

Subtract b from both sides

$$cy - b = ax$$

Divide through by x

$$\frac{cy - b}{x} = a$$

Thus

$$a = \frac{cy - b}{x}$$

Example 4.5

Make x the subject of $y = x^{1/2} + 1$

($x^{1/2}$ means the square root of x, that is the number which when multiplied by itself equals x.)

Subtract 1 from both sides

$$y - 1 = x^{1/2}$$

Square both sides of the equation
$$(y - 1)^2 = (x^{1/2})^2$$
Thus
$$(y - 1)^2 = x^{1/2 \times 2} \text{ (multiple powers)}$$
$$= x$$
and
$$x = (y - 1)^2$$
or
$$x = y^2 - 2y + 1$$
(see example 3.5).

Note a new aid to transposition is used here, the squaring of both sides of an equation to remove a square root. This is quite in order since if two quantities are equal then clearly their squares must be equal.

Example 4.6

Make R_2 the subject of $R_T = \dfrac{R_1 R_2}{R_1 + R_2}$

Multiply both sides by $(R_1 + R_2)$
$$R_T (R_1 + R_2) = R_1 R_2$$

The required subject is now on both sides of the equation. Terms containing R must be gathered together on one side. Expand the bracket to obtain the term containing R_2 on the left-hand side
$$R_T R_1 + R_T R_2 = R_1 R_2$$
Subtract $R_T R_2$ from both sides
$$R_T R_1 = R_1 R_2 - R_T R_2$$
Use brackets to extract R_2
$$R_T R_1 = (R_1 - R_T) R_2$$
Divide through by $(R_1 - R_T)$
$$\frac{R_T R_1}{R_1 - R_T} = R_2$$

Exercise 4.1

Make the variable shown the subject in the following formulae

(1) a in $x = \dfrac{ay}{b}$

(2) x in $xy + c = cy$

(3) t in $V = u + at$

(4) T_1 in $R_1 = R_0 (1 + \alpha T_1)$

(5) b in $x = \dfrac{1}{b} - c$ (8) c in $a = b^{1/2}c^{1/2}$

(6) i in $P = i^2R$ (9) x in $z = x^2 - y^2$

(7) l in $R = \rho\dfrac{l}{A}$ (10) R_1 in $R_T = \dfrac{R_1 R_2}{R_1 + R_2}$

EVALUATION OF FORMULAE

Having obtained the formula with the required subject it may then be necessary to find the value of the variable which is the subject for given values of the other variables. Sometimes in such cases the subject variable is referred to as the *dependent* variable (since it depends on the values of the other variables) and the other variables as the *independent* variables.

Thus, in the formula $R_T = R_1 R_2/(R_1 + R_2)$ for example (in which R_T represents total resistance of two resistors having resistance R_1 and R_2 connected in parallel), R_T is the dependent variable and R_1, R_2 independent variables.

Evaluation of a formula is fairly straightforward and all that is required is to write in the given values for the variables and calculate the value of the subject using logarithms or slide rule. In most practical examples multiples or submultiples of units using powers of 10 are involved, for examples milliamps, microvolts, etc., and care must be taken to insert the correct multiplier. Care must also be taken to ensure that in engineering formulae the correct consistent units are used throughout.

Example 4.7

The value of the resultant resistance R_T when two resistors having resistance R_1, R_2 are connected in parallel is

$$R_T = \frac{R_1 R_2}{R_1 + R_2}$$

where R_T, R_1 and R_2 are all measured in ohms.

Calculate R_T to three significant figures when $R_1 = 1$ kΩ and $R_2 = 1200$ Ω

$$R_T = \frac{1000 \times 1200}{1000 + 1200} \quad \text{(writing 1 k}\Omega \text{ as 1000 } \Omega)$$

$$= 545 \ \Omega \qquad \text{(slide rule)}$$

Example 4.8

The periodic time of a pendulum of length l metres is given by

$$T = \frac{1}{2\pi} \sqrt{\frac{l}{g}} \text{ seconds}$$

where g is the acceleration due to gravity (9.81 m/s^2) and π is a constant equal to 3.14. Find T when $l = 25$ cm.

As stated, when using the formula l must be in metres. Now $l = 25$ cm, that is 25×10^{-2} m or 0.25 m. Thus

$$T = \frac{1}{2 \times 3.14}\sqrt{\frac{0.25}{9.81}}$$

$$= 0.0254 \text{ s}$$

The answer could also be written as 25.5×10^{-3} s or 25.5 ms (milliseconds).

Example 4.9

The power P in an electrical circuit in terms of the circuit resistance R and the current I is given by the equation $P = I^2R$ where P is measured in watts, I in amps and R in ohms. Calculate the current in milliamps which flows in a circuit of resistance 4.7 kilohms when the power is 500 milliwatts.

First we must make I the subject of the formula $P = I^2R$. Divide by R on both sides

$$\frac{P}{R} = I^2$$

Take the square root of each side

$$I = \sqrt{\frac{P}{R}}$$

Now

$$P = 500 \text{ mW which is } 0.5 \text{ W}$$

and

$$R = 4.7 \text{ k}\Omega \text{ which is } 4700 \ \Omega$$

Thus

$$I = \sqrt{\frac{0.5}{4700}}$$

$$= \sqrt{\left(\frac{5000}{4700} \times 10^{-4}\right)}$$

Note the use of the multiplier 10^{-4} to make the placing of the decimal point easier.

$$= \sqrt{(1.063 \times 10^{-4})}$$

$$= 1.03 \times 10^{-2}$$

(Find the square root of 1.063 and halve the index of the multiplier.)

$$= 10.3 \times 10^{-3}$$

(Move the decimal point to obtain the right multiplier for mA.)

$$I = 10.3 \text{ mA}$$

Exercise 4.2

(1) Calculate R_T (ohms) in the formula of example 4.7 when $R_1 = 1$ MΩ and $R_2 = 500$ kΩ.

(2) Calculate R_1 (ohms) in the formula of example 4.7 when $R_T = 1$ kΩ and $R_1 = 1.5$ kΩ.

(3) The combined capacitance C_T (farads) of two capacitors of capacitance C_1 and C_2 (farads) is given by

$$C_T = \frac{1}{\dfrac{1}{C_1} + \dfrac{1}{C_2}}$$

Find C_T in microfarads when $C_1 = 500$ pF, $C_2 = 1000$ pF.

(4) Calculate R_0 in the formula of example 4.3 when $R_1 = 132.5$ Ω, $T_1 = 50°$C and $\alpha = 0.0002$.

(5) Calculate R in the formula of example 4.1 if $l = 51.3$ m, $A = 0.02$ cm^2 and $\rho = 0.001$ Ωm.

(6) Calculate T in the formula of example 4.8 when $l = 0.35$ m. Take $g = 9.81$ m/s^2 and $\pi = 3.14$.

(7) Calculate l in the formula of example 4.8 if $T = 0.1$ s, $g = 9.81$ m/s^2 and $\pi = 3.14$.

SIMPLE LINEAR EQUATIONS

A linear equation is one in which an unknown quantity represented by a symbol is raised only to the power unity, that is if the quantity is x then only terms involving x are contained in the equation—terms involving x^2, x^3, etc. do not appear. Solution of these equations, that is finding the value of x which makes the equation valid ('satisfies the equation'), is obtained by gathering together like terms and making x the subject of the equation. With this kind of equation there is only *one* value of x which satisfies the equation.

Example 4.9

Solve the following equation for x

$$4x - 5 + 7x - 3 = 2x - 18 - x$$

First simplify both sides of the equation by gathering together all terms containing x and all constants and then perform addition, subtraction, etc. as required. Thus

$$11x - 8 = x - 18$$

Now adjust the equation so that all terms containing x are on the left-hand side of the equation and all constants are on the right-hand side.

Add 8 to both sides

$$11x - 8 + 8 = x - 18 + 8$$

thus

$$11x = x - 10$$

Subtract x from both sides

$$11x - x = x - x - 10$$

and

$$10x = -10$$

Divide both sides by 10

$$x = -1$$

Check by substitution of $x = -1$ in the *original* equation.

Left-hand side (LHS) of the original equation $= 11x - 8$ and when $x = -1$ it has the value $11(-1) - 8$, that is $-11 - 8$ or -19.

Right-hand side (RHS) of the original equation $= x - 18$ and when $x = -1$ it has the value $-1 - 18$ or -19.

Since the value of the RHS = the value of the LHS when $x = -1$, this is the correct answer.

A rule to aid simplification is apparent from this example. This is that terms may be removed from one side of an equation and placed on the other provided that their signs are reversed. Thus 8 in the LHS of the original equation becomes -8 in the RHS. (What in fact is being done here is the subtraction of 8 from both sides.)

The solution of an equation need not be written out in the detail of example 4.9. This was done to clarify the method. The following example has an adequate layout.

Example 4.10

Solve for y when

$$18y - 15 + y = y - 12 + 3y - 6$$

LHS is $19y - 15$ and RHS is $4y - 18$. Thus

$$19y - 15 = 4y - 18$$
$$19y - 4y = 15 - 18$$
$$15y = -3$$

and

$$y = -\frac{3}{15}$$

$$= -\frac{1}{5}$$

Check in original equation

when $y = -\frac{1}{5}$

$$\text{LHS} = -\frac{18}{5} - 15 - \frac{1}{5}$$

$$= -\frac{19}{5} - 15$$

$$= \frac{-19 - 75}{5}$$

$$= \frac{-94}{5}$$

and

$$\text{RHS} = -\frac{1}{5} - 12 - \frac{3}{5} - 6$$

$$= \frac{-1 - 60 - 3 - 30}{5}$$

$$= \frac{-94}{5}$$

Thus since LHS = RHS the answer is correct.

If sufficient care is taken in this type of example a wrong answer can be corrected by a check as shown.

Example 4.11

Solve for *a* when $15 = \frac{2a - 6}{3a + 6}$

Multiply both sides by $(3a + 6)$ to give
$$15(3a + 6) = 2a - 6$$

Expand the LHS
$$45a + 90 = 2a - 6$$
$$45a - 2a = -90 - 6$$
$$43a = -96$$

therefore

$$a = -\frac{96}{43}$$

Check in original equation

$$\text{LHS} = 15$$

$$\text{RHS} = \frac{-2(96/43) - 6}{-3(96/43) + 6}$$

Multiply every term in both numerator and denominator by 43 (this leaves the value unchanged) to give

$$\text{RHS} = \frac{-192 - 258}{-288 + 258}$$

$$= \frac{-450}{-30}$$

$$= 15$$

Example 4.12

Solve for x when $\sqrt{\left(\dfrac{x - 5 + 4x}{6 - x}\right)} = 5$

This does not appear to be a linear equation. It can be made so however since if both sides are squared no terms containing powers of x other than 1 are apparent. Thus

$$\frac{x - 5 + 4x}{6 - x} = 25$$

(Notice that squaring the LHS merely removes the root sign.)
Multiply through by $6 - x$

$$x - 5 + 4x = 25(6 - x)$$
$$x - 5 + 4x = 150 - 25x$$
$$5x - 5 = 150 - 25x$$

therefore

$$5x + 25x = 150 + 5$$
$$30x = 155$$
$$x = \frac{155}{30}$$

that is

$$x = \frac{31}{6} \text{ (dividing through by 5)}$$

Check original equation for $x = 31/6$

LHS is the square root of

$$\frac{\dfrac{31}{6} - 5 + 4\left(\dfrac{31}{6}\right)}{6 - \left(\dfrac{31}{6}\right)}$$

Multiply throughout (all terms) by 6 to give

$$\frac{31 - 30 + 124}{36 - 31}$$

that is 125/5 or 25 and the square root of 25 is 5. RHS is 5; the answer is therefore correct.

Example 4.13

Solve the equation $\dfrac{4}{x - 3} = \dfrac{6}{4 - x}$

Multiply both sides by $(4 - x)$ to give

$$\frac{4(4 - x)}{x - 3} = 6$$

Multiply both sides by $(x - 3)$ to give

$$4(4 - x) = 6(x - 3)$$

(Alternatively, turn both sides 'upside-down' to give

$$\frac{x - 3}{4} = \frac{4 - x}{6}$$

and multiply through by 24 to give $6(x - 3) = 4(4 - x)$.)
Expand brackets

$$16 - 4x = 6x - 18$$

gathering terms

$$34 = 10x$$

and

$$x = \frac{34}{10} = \frac{17}{5}$$

Check LHS of equation using $x = 17/5$ is

$$\frac{4}{\dfrac{17}{5} - 3} = \frac{20}{17 - 15}$$

$$= 10$$

RHS of equation using this value of x is

$$\frac{6}{4 - \dfrac{17}{5}} = \frac{30}{20 - 17}$$

$$= 10$$

Therefore the answer $x = 17/5$ is correct.

Exercise 4.3

Solve the following equations for x

(1) $\dfrac{3}{x-2} = \dfrac{5}{x+1}$

(2) $15x = 31x - 6 + 2x$

(3) $\dfrac{x+7}{5} = \dfrac{x-9}{3}$

(4) $2x = 9 - 7x + 3$

Solve the following equations for y

(5) $y = 9y + 10 - 3y - 7$

(6) $\dfrac{7}{y+7} = 7$

(7) Solve

$\dfrac{a}{3-a} = 10$ for a

(8) Find b in the equation

$8(b-7) = \dfrac{2b+5}{3}$

(9) Find c in the equation

$4c(2c - 7 + 5c - 7c) = 17$

(10) Find x in the equation

$\dfrac{4}{3+x} \quad \dfrac{5}{x-1} = \dfrac{9}{x+18}$

SIMULTANEOUS LINEAR EQUATIONS

If a linear equation exists connecting two unknown quantities then both quantities are variable, the value of the one being determined by the other. Thus, in an equation such as $y = 4 - x$ for example, any value may be given to x and this in turn will determine the value of y for that value of x. For example if $x = 1$ then $y = 4 - 1$, that is 3; if $x = 2$ then $y = 2$; if $x = 3$ then $y = 1$, and so on.

Often in engineering problems there exist two or more unknown quantities each of which has only *one* value, that value being determined by the value of the others. In these cases one equation is insufficient to determine the value of each of the unknown quantities. It is found that for two unknown quantities having only one value each then two linear equations are required, for three unknowns then three linear equations are required and, in general, the number of linear equations needed to find the value of each unknown is equal to the number of unknowns. An example of such *simultaneous linear equations* occurs in electrical engineering when it is desired to find the value of individual electric currents flowing in a circuit containing more than one current path.

It is necessary to be able to solve such simultaneous linear equations, the method generally being to obtain one linear equation containing only one of the unknowns and then to proceed as in the previous section. In this section we shall restrict the number of unknowns to two.

The method of obtaining the one equation containing one unknown from the given two equations may use either substitution or elimination.

Substitution With this method one unknown is expressed in terms of the other using one of the given equations and the resultant expression is then substituted in the other of the two given equations.

Example 4.14

Find the values of x and y which satisfy both given equations simultaneously

$$x - y = 3 \tag{4.1}$$
$$4x + y = 6 \tag{4.2}$$

From equation 4.1

$$y = x - 3$$

Substitute for y in equation 4.2

$$4x + (x - 3) = 6$$
$$4x + x - 3 = 6$$
$$5x = 9$$

Thus

$$x = \frac{9}{5}$$

and since $y = 6 - 4x$ from 4.2

$$y = 6 - 4 \left(\frac{9}{5} \right)$$
$$= \frac{30 - 36}{5}$$
$$= -\frac{6}{5}$$

The values of x and y which satisfy both equations simultaneously are

$$x = \frac{9}{5} \qquad y = -\frac{6}{5}$$

Since equation 4.2 was used to find y once x was known, use equation 4.1 to check the answer.

LHS of equation inserting values is

$$\frac{9}{5} - \left(-\frac{6}{5} \right)$$

that is

$$\frac{9}{5} + \frac{6}{5} = \frac{15}{5}$$
$$= 3$$

RHS of equation inserting values is also 3; therefore the answer is correct. (As with the previous examples the risk of getting a wrong answer is much reduced by checking using the given equations.)

Elimination With this method one of the unknown quantities is eliminated by making the coefficient of the quantity the same numerically in each equation and then adding or subtracting as appropriate. As before the idea is to obtain *one* linear equation with only one unknown.

Using the above example to demonstrate: the coefficient of y is numerically the same in both equations. Add equation 4.1 to equation 4.2.

$$x - y + 4x + y = 3 + 6$$
$$5x = 9$$

(since y is eliminated)

$$x = \frac{9}{5}$$

and from 4.1 by substitution of this value of x

$$\frac{9}{5} - y = 3$$
$$y = \frac{9}{5} - 3$$
$$= -\frac{6}{5}$$

as before.

Again, since equation 4.1 was used to find y once x was known, then equation 4.2 is used as a check. The check has been done above and so will not be repeated.

Example 4.15

Solve the following equations for x and y

$$4x + 3y = 5 \tag{4.3}$$
$$2x + 5y = 10 \tag{4.4}$$

Elimination of y is achieved as follows

Multiply equation 4.3 throughout by 5 (the coefficient of y in equation 4.4)

$$20x + 15y = 25 \tag{4.5}$$

Multiply equation 4.4 throughout by 3 (the coefficient of y in equation 4.3)

$$6x + 15y = 30 \tag{4.6}$$

The coefficients of y in equations 4.5 and 4.6 are now the same. Subtract equation 4.6 from equation 4.5.

$$20x + 15y - 6x - 15y = 25 - 30$$
$$14x = -5$$
$$x = -\frac{5}{14}$$

Substitute this value of x in equation 4.3

$$4\left(-\frac{5}{14}\right) + 3y = 5$$

$$-\frac{20}{14} + 3y = 5$$

$$3y = 5 + \frac{10}{7}$$

(dividing $-20/14$ through by 2 and transferring to the other side.)

$$3y = \frac{35 + 10}{7}$$

$$3y = \frac{45}{7}$$

therefore

$$y = \frac{45}{21} = \frac{15}{7}$$

Equation 4.3 was used to find y. Use equation 4.4 to check

$$\text{LHS} = 2\left(-\frac{5}{14}\right) + 5\left(\frac{15}{7}\right)$$

$$= -\frac{5}{7} + \frac{75}{7}$$

$$= +\frac{70}{7}$$

$$= 10$$

$$\text{RHS} = 10$$

The answer is $x = -5/14$, $y = 15/7$.

Example 4.16

Solve for x and y

$$\frac{x}{5} + \frac{y}{3} = \frac{4}{7} \tag{4.7}$$

$$\frac{x}{9} - \frac{y}{6} = \frac{5}{18} \tag{4.8}$$

The best method to reduce the possibility of error is to change the fractional coefficients to whole numbers.

Multiply equation 4.7 throughout by 105 (the LCM of 5, 3 and 7).

$$\frac{105x}{5} + \frac{105y}{3} = \frac{105 \times 4}{7}$$

$$21x + 35y = 60 \qquad\qquad (4.9)$$

Multiply equation 4.8 throughout by 18 (the LCM of 9, 6 and 18).

$$2x - 3y = 5 \qquad\qquad (4.10)$$

Multiply equation 4.9 throughout by 3 (the coefficient of y in equation 4.10)

$$63x + 105y = 180 \qquad\qquad (4.11)$$

Multiply equation 4.10 throughout by 35 (the coefficient of y in equation 4.9)

$$70x - 105y = 175 \qquad\qquad (4.12)$$

Add equations 4.11 and 4.12 to eliminate y

$$133x = 355$$

$$x = \frac{355}{133}$$

Rather than continue with unwieldy fractions convert to decimal mixed-numbers (using a slide rule or logarithms). Thus $x = 2.665$ or 2.67 to two places.

Substitute this value of x in equation 4.9 to find y.

$$21 \times 2.67 + 35y = 60$$

$$56.1 + 35y = 60$$

$$y = \frac{60 - 56.1}{35}$$

$$= 0.111 \text{ or } 0.11 \text{ to two places}$$

Check using equation 4.10. LHS is $2x - 3y$, that is

$$2 \times 2.67 - 3 \times 0.110$$

which is $5.34 - 0.330$, approximately 5. RHS = 5.

Note that conversion to decimals inevitably introduces a degree of approximation as shown in the checking procedure. The check will still indicate whether or not the values are correct (to within the selected degree of accuracy, that is two decimal places).

The answer is $x = 2.67$, $y = 0.11$.

Exercise 4.4

Solve the following simultaneous equations for the variables shown

(1) $3x + y = 7$
      $x - y = 10$

(2) $4a = 7 - y$
      $5a + y = 8$

(3) $a = b - 3$
      $5a + 3 = 2b$

(4) $\dfrac{4}{x - y} = 7$

      $\dfrac{3}{x + y} = 8$

(5) $9x(3 - y) = 5$
      $4x + 9xy = 7$

(6) $\dfrac{a - b}{7} = \dfrac{2a + b}{8}$

      $3a - b = 9$

(7) $4x = \dfrac{y + 5}{7}$

      $y = \dfrac{x - 4}{3}$

RATIO AND PROPORTION

A ratio of two numbers means one divided by the other. If a quantity is measured more than once under different circumstances, for example the electrical resistance of a wire when cold and when hot, a comparison may be made of the measurements using a ratio. Problems involving ratio are very often solved by the application of simple algebra and it is for this reason that discussion of the topic is included in this chapter.

To return to the example mentioned, suppose the resistance R_1 of a wire at a certain temperature is 40 Ω and the resistance R_2 of the wire at a higher temperature is 20 Ω, then the ratio of the resistances written as

$$R_2 : R_1 \text{ or } \frac{R_2}{R_1}$$

is equal to the ratio of the numbers, written as

$$20 : 40 \text{ or } \frac{20}{40}$$

that is

$$\frac{R_2}{R_1} = \frac{20}{40}$$

or 1/2 (dividing through by 20).

A ratio does not necessarily give actual values. The ratio 20/40 above for instance may be simplified to a ratio 1/2. Before simplification the figures quoted (20 and 40) are the actual values but the simplified ratio figures (1 and 2) are not. Resistance measurements of 30 and 60, or 10 and 20, or

200 and 400 taken under the conditions described would all have the same ratio of 1/2 since

$$\frac{30}{60} = \frac{10}{20} = \frac{200}{400} = \frac{1}{2}$$

Notice also that since a ratio is a comparison of two measurements of the same quantity and the units of both measurements are the same, the ratio itself has no units.

Example 4.17

The ratio of two resistance values R_1 and R_2 is given by $R_1 : R_2 = 5 : 6$. If R_1 is 200 Ω find the value of R_2.

$$\frac{R_1}{R_2} = \frac{5}{6}$$

Making R_2 the subject of the equation

$$R_2 = \frac{6}{5} R_1$$

$$= \frac{6 \times 200}{5}$$

$$= 240 \ \Omega$$

Example 4.18

A piece of resistance wire 500 mm long is divided into two lengths in the ratio 7 : 4. Find the lengths of the two pieces.

Let $7x$ mm be the length of one piece (where x is unknown). Then for the ratio of the two lengths to be 7 : 4 the other length must be $4x$ mm, that is $7x/4x = 7/4$.

Total length $= 7x + 4x$
but total length $= 500$ mm
thus

$$7x + 4x = 500$$

(a simple linear equation)
and

$$11x = 500$$

so that

$$x = \frac{500}{11} = 45.45$$

Thus one length is 7×45.45 mm, that is 318.15 mm and the other length is $500 - 318.15 = 181.85$ mm. (Alternatively, the other length is $4 \times 45.45 = 181.8$ mm, the difference in answer being due to the fact that 45.45 is an approximation to two decimal places.)

Example 4.19

The ratio of two voltages V_1 and V_2 is $V_1/V_2 = 4/5$. The ratio of voltage V_2 to a third voltage V_3 is $V_2/V_3 = 7/8$. Find the ratio of voltage V_1 to voltage V_3.

Now

$$\frac{V_1}{V_2} = \frac{4}{5}$$

and

$$\frac{V_2}{V_3} = \frac{7}{8}$$

Therefore

$$\frac{V_1}{V_2} \times \frac{V_2}{V_3} = \frac{4}{5} \times \frac{7}{8}$$

Dividing through the left-hand side by V_2 gives

$$\frac{V_1}{V_3} = \frac{7}{10}$$

which is the required answer.

Example 4.20

A voltage from a certain supply is reduced by 22 per cent when a load is connected. Find the ratio between the no-load voltage V_{NL} and the load voltage V_L.

A reduction of 22 per cent means that the load voltage falls by 22/100 of its no-load value. Then load voltage $= (1 - 22/100)$ of no-load voltage or

$$V_L = \left(1 - \frac{22}{100}\right) V_{NL}$$

$$V_L = \frac{88}{100} V_{NL}$$

Thus by rearranging the formula*

$$\frac{V_{NL}}{V_L} = \frac{100}{88} = 1.137 \text{ (slide rule)}$$

Example 4.21

A transformer winding is tapped in two places such that the ratio of the number of turns in each section, represented by N_1, N_2 and N_3, is given by $N_1 : N_2 : N_3 = 1 : 2 : 3$. The total number of turns is 600. Find the number of turns per section.

---

*The rearrangement is made by multiplying both sides by 100, dividing both sides by 88, then dividing both sides by V_L.

The statement $N_1 : N_2 : N_3 = 1 : 2 : 3$ means that

$$\frac{N_1}{N_2} = \frac{1}{2} \qquad \frac{N_2}{N_3} = \frac{2}{3} \qquad \frac{N_1}{N_3} = \frac{1}{3}$$

and we are told that

$$N_1 + N_2 + N_3 = 600$$

Replace N_2 by $2N_1$ since

$$\frac{N_1}{N_2} = \frac{1}{2}$$

and therefore

$$N_1 = \frac{1}{2}N_2 \text{ or } N_2 = 2N_1$$

Replace N_3 by $3N_1$ since

$$\frac{N_1}{N_3} = \frac{1}{3}$$

and therefore

$$N_1 = \frac{1}{3}N_3 \text{ or } N_3 = 3N_1$$

and we have

$$N_1 + 2N_1 + 3N_1 = 600$$

Thus

$$6N_1 = 600$$
$$N_1 = 100 \text{ turns}$$

Therefore

$$N_2 = 200 \text{ turns}$$
$$N_3 = 300 \text{ turns}$$

(This problem was actually a solution of three simultaneous equations to find the value of three unknowns. The method used was substitution.)

Example 4.22

An alloy contains three different metals A, B and C in the ratio $7 : 5 : 4$ by mass. Find the mass of metal C in 240 g of the alloy.

The information given states that the ratio

$$\text{mass of } A : \text{mass of } B : \text{mass of } C = 7 : 5 : 4$$

Let the mass of A be $7x$ g so that the mass of B will be $5x$ g and the mass of C will be $4x$ g.
Thus

$$7x + 5x + 4x = 240$$
$$16x = 240$$

therefore

$$x = \frac{240}{16} = 15$$

The mass of C in 240 g is therefore 4×15, that is 60 g.

Further problems on ratio are included in exercise 4.5.

If the ratio between two variable quantities is constant whatever values they may have it is said that the one variable quantity is *directly proportional* to the other. The symbol for direct proportion is $\propto$. Thus, if the ratio y/x is constant, then y is directly proportional to x and this is written

$$y \propto x$$

which implies that if for example the value of x is doubled then the value of y will be doubled, if x is trebled in value y is trebled in value, if x is halved in value y is halved in value, and so on.

If the ratio between one variable quantity and the *reciprocal* of another variable quantity is constant it is said that the first variable is *inversely* or *indirectly proportional* to the second variable. For example if $y : 1/x$ is constant then y is inversely or indirectly proportional to x. In this case, if x is doubled, y is halved and vice versa or if x is multiplied by 3, y is divided by 3. Examples of proportional relationships are given below. Conversely, if it is known that one variable is inversely or directly proportional to another then the equation relating the variables can be deduced. For if $y \propto x$ then $y = $ constant $\times x$ or if $y \propto 1/x$ then $y = $ constant$/x$. Use of this fact is also demonstrated in the examples.

Example 4.23

The resistance R of a piece of wire is directly proportional to its length l and inversely proportional to its cross-sectional area a. Deduce the equation relating R, l and a and state what would happen to the resistance of a piece of wire if its length and cross-sectional area were doubled.

The equation is

$$R = \frac{\text{constant} \times l}{a}$$

If the length is doubled, other variables remaining constant, the resistance is doubled. If the area is doubled, other variables remaining constant, the resistance is halved. The combined effect of both doubling the resistance and halving the area is therefore to keep the value of the resistance the same.

Using symbols, if

$$R = \text{constant} \times \frac{l}{a}$$

and l is changed to $2l$ and a to $2a$, then

$$\text{new resistance} = \text{constant} \times \frac{2l}{2a}$$

$$= \text{constant} \times \frac{l}{a}$$

$$= R$$

Example 4.24

A piece of wire of uniform cross-section is uniformly expanded to twice its length while keeping the volume constant. Determine how the resistance is changed using the relationship of example 4.23.

Now volume = length × area (see chapter 6). Thus if the volume remains the same and the length is doubled then the area must be halved.
Thus if

$$R = \text{constant} \times \frac{l}{a} \text{(using the symbols above)}$$

then

$$\text{new resistance} = \text{constant} \times \frac{2l}{\frac{1}{2}a}$$

$$= 4 \times \left(\text{constant} \times \frac{l}{a}\right)$$

$$= 4R$$

The resistance is quadrupled.

Example 4.25

For an electrical circuit of constant resistance the power absorbed by the circuit is proportional to the square of the current flowing in the circuit. Determine the ratio of the corresponding power-levels when the current is progressively increased in the ratio $5 : 4 : 3 : 2 : 1$.

Another way of stating what is required in this problem is to find the proportional increase in power as the current is progressively doubled, trebled, quadrupled and quintupled (that is multiplied by 2, 3, 4 and 5 respectively).
    Since

$$\text{power} \propto \text{current}^2$$

when the current is multiplied by 2 the power is multiplied by 4; when the current is multiplied by 3 the power is multiplied by 9; when the current is multiplied by 4 the power is multiplied by 16; and when the current is multiplied by 5 the power is multiplied by 25.
    The corresponding ratio of power levels to a ratio of current levels of $5 : 4 : 3 : 2 : 1$ is therefore $25 : 16 : 9 : 4 : 1$.

Exercise 4.5

(1) A piece of resistance wire 250 mm long is divided in the ratio $5 : 4 : 3 : 1$. Find the length of each part.

(2) The ratio of two voltages $V_1 : V_2$ is 25. Find the value of V_1 when $V_2 = 3$ V.

(3) The ratio of two currents $I_1 : I_2$ is $9 : 2$. The ratio of currents $I_2 : I_3$ is $15 : 7$. Find the ratio $I_3 : I_1$.

(4) A certain supply voltage is reduced in the ratio $50 : 47$ when a load is connected. Determine the percentage reduction in the no-load value of voltage caused by the load connection.

(5) If $x \propto yz$ find the ratio of the new value of x to the original when y is trebled and z is doubled.

(6) If $R \propto l$ and $R \propto 1/a$ and $l = 0.53$, $a = 0.02$ when $R = 100$ find the value of the constant in the equation relating R, l and a.

(7) Two pieces of wire have lengths l_1, l_2 and cross-sectional areas a_1, a_2 respectively. The resistance of each piece of wire is proportional to length and inversely proportional to cross-sectional area and has the same value. If $l_1 : l_2 = 3 : 2$ find $a_1 : a_2$.

5 Graphs

In the previous chapters we have discussed equations involving one variable quantity, for example x or y, a or b, etc., and equations involving two variable quantities, for example x *and* y, a *and* b, etc. The first kind was discussed in the section entitled simple linear equations, the second in the section entitled simultaneous linear equations. Before considering the meaning and purpose of a graph in engineering let us briefly re-examine the words 'linear' and 'simultaneous' as used above. Linear means that the power to which the variable or variables are raised throughout is unity, that is equations containing x^2, y^2, x^3, etc. are *not* linear equations. The reason for the use of the word linear will become apparent in this chapter. Simultaneous used in the mathematical context means that the equations given are valid at the same time. This simply means that for two such equations involving two unknowns (or three such equations involving three unknowns, etc.) there is only one value of each variable which satisfies all the equations simultaneously. (This applies equally to one equation containing only one variable, but there is then no need for the use of the word 'simultaneous'.)

If only one equation relating two variable quantities is available then no single solution for each variable is the only one. For example the equations

$$x - y = 3$$
$$4x + y = 6$$

(as given in example 4.14) when they exist simultaneously are both satisfied at the same time when $x = 9/5$ and $y = -6/5$, but either one of these equations on its own is satisfied by a whole series of pairs of values for the variables concerned.

Consider $x - y = 3$ for example. Rewriting as

$$y = x - 3$$

when

$$x = 1 \quad y = -2$$
$$x = 2 \quad y = -1$$
$$x = 3 \quad y = 0$$
$$x = 4 \quad y = 1$$

and so on. No single pair of values is the only pair. Only when another equation is involved which must be satisfied simultaneously, does a single pair of values become the unique solution.

In engineering there are many situations in which the value of one quantity determines the value of another, the relationship between the two quantities being described by an equation. In the cases where there is only one equation and two variable quantities there are many sets of values which satisfy the equation and it is useful to show these values in pictorial form using a *graph*. The shape of the graph is determined by the equation and more often than not the process works the other way round, in that from the shape of a given graph obtained by experimental observation the equation relating the variable quantities may be deduced. This can then be used to predict values of the variables in a situation which has not actually been observed. This fact is especially useful in cases where such observation might be dangerous either to equipment or personnel or both.

Consider the equation $y = 2x$. In this equation y is the subject and is called the dependent variable, x is called the independent variable (see p. 90). In any such equation where y is the dependent variable y is said to be a *function* of x since the value of y is determined by the value of x. Similarly, in $a = 3b + 4$, a is a function of b or in $p = 3q - 2$, p is a function of q. Having looked at the terms used, now let us examine the techniques used in drawing graphs.

Some values of x and y which satisfy the equation $y = 2x$ are as follows

y	2	4	6	8	10	0	−2	−4	−6	−8	−10
x	1	2	3	4	5	0	−1	−2	−3	−4	− 5

Such an arrangement is called a *table of values*. In practical examples the table should show, next to the variable, what units if any the variable is being measured in. For this equation the graph must be able to show that when x is 1, y is 2, when x is 2, y is 4 when x is −1, y is −2 and so on. We must therefore have some means of showing both positive and negative values of both variables.

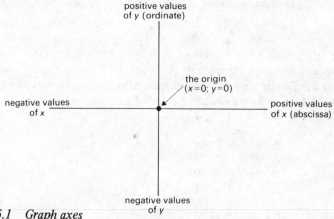

Figure 5.1   Graph axes

The usual arrangement is shown in figure 5.1. Two lines called *axes* are drawn, one vertical and one horizontal, their point of intersection being called the *origin.* Values of one variable are marked along one axis, values of the other being marked on the other axis. The variable marked along the horizontal axis is called the *abscissa* and that marked on the vertical axis is called the *ordinate.* Positive values of the abscissa are marked to the right of the origin, negative values to the left. Positive values of the ordinate are marked above the origin, negative values below. When x and y are used as symbols for variable quantities y is usually (but not always) taken as ordinate and x as abscissa.

As shown the graph area is divided into four quarters. These are called *quadrants.* In the upper right-hand quadrant values of both variables are positive, in the lower left-hand quadrant they are negative. In the upper left-hand quadrant the ordinate variable has positive values and the abscissa variable negative values and in the lower right-hand quadrant the ordinate has negative values and the abscissa positive. Not all quadrants need be drawn depending on the values that are to be plotted; for example if only positive values of both variables are to be plotted then only the upper right-hand quadrant need be drawn. When all four quadrants are used the point where the axes cross one another—the origin—is the point where both variables have the value zero. If only one quadrant is used this need not necessarily be so, depending on what values are to be plotted. (There would be little point for example, in starting the x scale at $x = 0$ if the given values lay between 200 and 250. This is further discussed in the section on equation deduction.)

The marking of the single point on the graph corresponding to each set of values of the variables is called *plotting* the values. Now examine figure 5.2 which plots the graph of $y = 2x$.

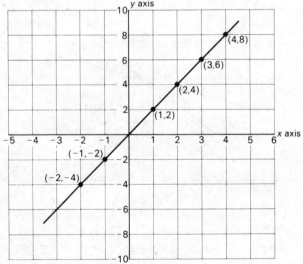

Figure 5.2   Graph of $y = 2x$

When $x = 0$, $y = 0$. One point on the graph is therefore the origin. When $x = 1$, $y = 2$. Where the vertical line running through $x = 1$ meets the horizontal line running through $y = 2$ is the point on the graph at which $x = 1$ and $y = 2$.

Note that graphs are usually plotted on special paper on which is printed a series of vertical and horizontal lines to help make placing the point easier. Not all such lines will be shown in the diagrams in this chapter in the interests of clarification of the diagrams.

Similarly, where the vertical line through $x = 2$ meets the horizontal line through $y = 4$ is the point on the graph where $x = 2$, $y = 4$.

Examine the graph for the remaining points and note how such a point may be indicated by writing the values of the variables in brackets with the abscissa value first. (It is not necessary to do this on an engineering graph. Such a practice would overfill the graph with figures and reduce the clarity. It is used here for demonstration.)

As can be seen, the graph of $y = 2x$ is a straight line and as such needs only two points to locate it. In fact, all graphs of linear equations, are straight lines and this is the reason for the use of the word linear.

The reader is advised to plot graphs of the following equations, which will be discussed in some detail. The table of values is given and figure 5.3 shows the shape of the graphs.

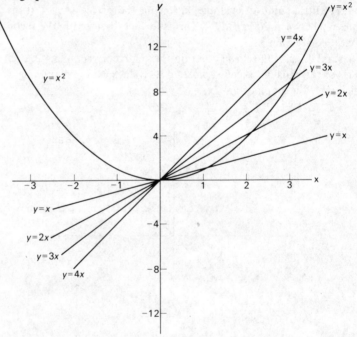

Figure 5.3   Graphs of $y = x$, $y = 2x$, $y = 3x$, $y = 4x$ and $y = x^2$

x	-3	-2	-1	0	1	2	3
$y = x$	-3	-2	-1	0	1	2	3
$y = 2x$	-6	-4	-2	0	2	4	6
$y = 3x$	-9	-6	-3	0	3	6	9
$y = 4x$	-12	-8	-4	0	4	8	12
$y = x^2$	9	4	1	0	1	4	9

From an examination of figure 5.3 the following points can be made

(1) The graph of $y = x^2$ is *not* a straight line but is a curve symmetrical about the y axis and passing through the origin.
(2) All the remaining graphs are straight lines passing through the origin.
(3) The slope of $y = 4x$ is greater than that of $y = 3x$, which is greater than that of $y = x$.

THE STRAIGHT-LINE GRAPH

As was stated above, all equations containing an independent variable raised only to a power 1, that is if the independent variable is x, and there are no terms containing x^2, x^3, etc., produce straight lines when plotted as graphs. The important characteristics of such graphs are first the slope or *gradient* of the graph, and second whether or not the graph passes through the origin and if it does not, where it crosses the ordinate axis. Knowledge of these characteristics enables us to deduce the equation of a straight-line graph when this is not known, that is on occasions when plotting a graph of experimentally observed values of two variable quantities produces a graph which is a straight line.

The gradient

The gradient or slope of any line is the ratio between the vertical rise or fall of the line from the horizontal over a measured horizontal distance to the value of this measured distance. Thus if for every 5 cm measured along the horizontal a line rises a vertically measured distance from the horizontal of 1 cm as shown in figure 5.4a then the gradient is said to be 1/5. If the line were to fall in a similar manner the gradient would then be taken as negative and equal to $-1/5$ (fig. 5.4b).*

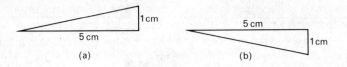

Figure 5.4   (a) Positive gradient +1/5. (b) Negative gradient $-1/5$

*A similar system is used when measuring road gradients but here the ratio is between the rise or fall of the road per distance measured along the road. Because of the relatively small gradients this latter distance is approximately equal to the distance travelled horizontally.

Consider the straight-line graphs shown in figure 5.3. Here the horizontal distance is a change in the value of x and the vertical rise or fall is the corresponding change in the value of y. Thus, for the graph of $y = x$ as x changes from $x = 0$ to $x = 3$, y changes from $y = 0$ to $y = 3$ and the ratio of vertical rise : horizontal distance equals 3 : 3 or 1—the gradient is unity.

Similarly for $y = 2x$ as x changes from 0 to 3, y changes from 0 to 6 and the gradient is 6/3 or 2. For $y = 3x$, the change in y of 9 (from $y = 0$ to $y = 9$) corresponds to a change in x of 3 (from $x = 0$ to $x = 3$) and the gradient is 9/3 or 3. Finally for $y = 4x$ the gradient is 12/3 or 4.

The gradient in each case is the coefficient of x and in general for equations of the form $y = mx$ (or $a = mb$ or $c = md$) where m is a constant and the other symbols represent variable quantities then m is the gradient of the graph.

Example 5.1

Find the gradients of the graphs of the following equations
(a) $y = 5x$ (b) $4y = 3x$ (c) $2y = -x$ (d) $7a = -6b$

(a)   The gradient is 5.
(b)   Rearrange $4y = 3x$ to give $y = 3/4x$. The gradient is 3/4.
(c)   Rearrange $2y = -x$ to give $y = -x/2$ (that is the coefficient of x is $-1/2$). The gradient is $-1/2$.
(d)   Rearrange $7a = -6b$ to give $a = -6b/7$. The gradient is $-6/7$.
In examples 5.1c and 5.1d the graphs slope downwards.

The intercept

The value of the variable at the point where the graph cuts one or other of the axes is called the *intercept* of the graph on the axis concerned. Thus if $x = 6$ at the point where $y = x - 6$ cuts the x axis then the intercept of this graph on the x axis is 6. Similarly if the graph cuts the y axis at $y = -6$ then the intercept on the y axis is -6. Knowledge of the intercept under certain conditions can help predict the equation connecting two variables when the graph plotting their relationship is available—for example from experimental observation.

The value of the intercept on either axis depends on the equation and on the situation of the axes relative to one another. In graphs using all quadrants the y (ordinate) axis crosses the x (abscissa) axis where $x = 0$ and similarly the x axis crosses the y axis where $y = 0$. The point of crossing, called the origin, is thus $x = 0, y = 0$. To find the intercept under these conditions all that is necessary is to put $x = 0$ in the equation to find the intercept on the y axis and $y = 0$ in the equation to find the intercept on the x axis. These intercept values, especially the intercept on the y axis when $x = 0$, are useful ones in deducing an equation from a graph—this will be discussed later. If either axis crosses the other at any other point, that is if the scale variable does not start at zero, then the intercept will be different and is not the value determined by putting $x = 0$ or $y = 0$ into the equation.

Consider the graphs of the following functions
$$y = x + 1 \quad y = x + 3 \quad y = x - 1$$
The table of values is

x	-2	-1	0	1	2
$y = x + 1$	-1	0	1	2	3
$y = x + 3$	1	2	3	4	5
$y = x - 1$	-3	-2	-1	0	1

(Only two values of x need be taken, the others are included as an additional emphasis that the graphs are straight lines.)

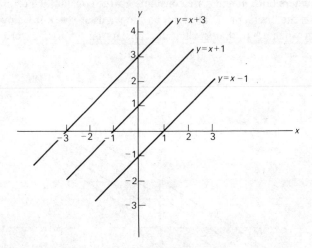

Figure 5.5   Graphs of $y = x + 3$, $y = x + 1$ and $y = x - 1$

The shape and position of these graphs relative to one another is shown in figure 5.5. As can be seen the graph of $y = x + 1$ cuts the y axis at $y = 1$, the graph of $y = x + 3$ cuts the y axis at $y = 3$ and the graph of $y = x - 1$ cuts the y axis at -1. Thus the intercepts on the y axis when $x = 0$ of these three graphs are 1, 3 and -1 respectively. Look at the values for $x = 0$ in the table above; this column gives the value of the intercepts of the three graphs. Thus by putting $x = 0$ into an equation relating y and x the intercept on the y axis may be found.

Similarly the intercept on the x axis, that is where the graph cuts the x axis, may be found by putting $y = 0$. These intercepts are $-1, -3$ and 1 for the three graphs as shown in the figure. If y is to be the subject of the equation however the y-axis intercept is the more important for reasons which follow.

Examination of the equations shows that when the equation is of the form where y is the subject on the LHS the constant which stands alone on the RHS is the y-axis intercept when $x = 0$. Thus when we are trying to deduce the equation relating two variable quantities from a graph of experimentally observed results, the intercept on the ordinate axis will be the constant on the RHS when the variable plotted as ordinate is on the LHS, has a coefficient of 1 and is raised to a power unity, provided that the abscissa scale begins at zero. This fact applies to all equations and graphs whether or not they are linear.

General equation of the straight-line graph

We have seen that for an equation of the form $y = mx$ where m is constant then the gradient of the graph is m. We have also seen that for an equation of the form $y = mx + c$ where both m and c are constants, c—the constant which stands alone without x—is the intercept of the graph on the y axis at $x = 0$. It follows from the last fact that when $c = 0$, that is when the constant on the RHS is zero (no

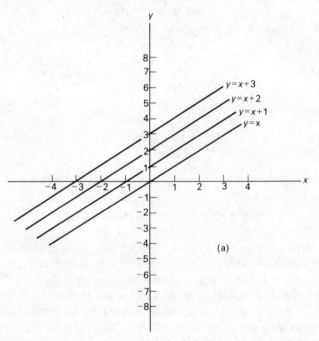

Figure 5.6a

constant is shown) the intercept is zero and the graph passes through the point $x = 0, y = 0$ (see the graphs shown in figure 5.3). It remains to be shown that for an equation of the form $y = mx + c$ the coefficient of x, that is m, is always the gradient. Figure 5.6a shows graphs of $y = x$, $y = x + 1$, $y = x + 2$ and $y = x + 3$; figure 5.6b shows graphs of $y = 2x$, $y = 2x + 1$, $y = 2x + 2$ and $y = 2x + 3$; as shown the gradient of all graphs in figure 5.6a is the same and equals the gradient of the graph of $y = x$, that is 1, and in figure 5.6b the gradient of all graphs

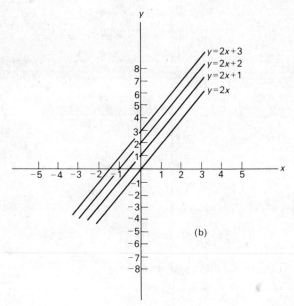

Figure 5.6b

is the same and equals the gradient of $y = 2x$, that is 2. The reader is advised to plot these graphs to verify the fact.

Thus the figures indicate that in any equation of the form $y = mx + c$, the gradient is always m and the y axis intercept at $x = 0$ is always c. Examples of half a dozen graphs do not constitute proof however. The proof is as follows. For the general equation $y = mx + c$ when x has some value x_1 let the value of y be y_1, that is

$$y_1 = mx_1 + c \qquad (5.1)$$

Similarly let y_2 be the value of y when x has the value x_2, then

$$y_2 = mx_2 + c \qquad (5.2)$$

Subtract equation 5.1 from 5.2

$$\begin{aligned} y_2 - y_1 &= mx_2 + c - mx_1 - c \\ &= mx_2 - mx_1 \\ &= m(x_2 - x_1) \end{aligned}$$

thus

$$\frac{y_2 - y_1}{x_2 - x_1} = m$$

but the LHS of this equation is the gradient, as shown in figure 5.7.

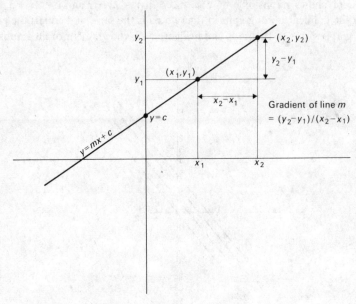

Figure 5.7   General equation of a straight line

Example 5.2

Find the gradient and the intercept on the y axis at $x = 0$ for the graphs of the following functions when y is plotted as ordinate and x as abscissa.

(a) $y = 3x + 5$ (d) $x - 3 = 2y$

(b) $5y = x + 3$

(c) $\dfrac{y}{4} = \dfrac{x}{5} - \dfrac{1}{3}$ (e) $4y + 7 = x$

(f) $3x + 4y + 7 = 0$

(a) The equation is already of the form $y = mx + c$, where $m = 3$ and $c = 5$.
Thus gradient is 3, y-axis intercept is 5.

(b) $5y = x + 3$
Divide by 5 throughout to give

$$y = \frac{x}{5} + \frac{3}{5}$$

Thus gradient is 1/5, y-axis intercept is 3/5.

(c) $\dfrac{y}{4} = \dfrac{x}{5} - \dfrac{1}{3}$

Multiply through by 4 to give

$$y = \frac{4x}{5} - \frac{4}{3}$$

Thus gradient is $4/5$, y-axis intercept is $-4/3$.

(d) $x - 3 = 2y$

Rearrange and divide through by 2 to give

$$y = \frac{x}{2} - \frac{3}{2}$$

Gradient is $1/2$, y-axis intercept is $-3/2$.

(e) $4y + 7 = x$

Subtract 7 from both sides and divide through by 4 to give

$$y = \frac{x}{4} - \frac{7}{4}$$

Gradient is $1/4$; y-axis intercept is $-7/4$.

(f) $3x + 4y + 7 = 0$

Subtract $(3x + 7)$ from both sides, divide through by 4 to give

$$y = -\frac{3x}{4} - \frac{7}{4}$$

Gradient is $-3/4$, y-axis intercept is $-7/4$.

Example 5.3

Find the gradient and intercepts on both axes for the graphs of the following functions when the variable shown is plotted as ordinate. Take the point where the axes cross as the point where both variables are zero.

(a) $a = 3b + 4$ a as ordinate
(b) $a = 3b + 4$ b as ordinate
(c) $4p = 2q + 5$ p as ordinate
(d) $4p = 2q + 5$ q as ordinate

In all cases arrange the equation in the form $y = mx + c$, that is in general

$$\text{ordinate} = m \times \text{abscissa} + c$$

(a) For $a = 3b + 4$, a ordinate, the gradient is 3, and the intercept on the a (ordinate) axis is 4.

To find the intercept on the b axis put $a = 0$ to give

$$0 = 3b + 4$$

that is

$$b = -\frac{4}{3}$$

(b) Rearrange $a = 3b + 4$ to put b on the LHS

$$3b = a - 4$$

$$b = \frac{a}{3} - \frac{4}{3}$$

Therefore gradient of $a = 3b + 4$ when b is the ordinate is 1/3 and intercept on the b axis is $-4/3$ as before. Intercept on the a axis is obtained by putting $b = 0$ in

$$b = \frac{a}{3} - \frac{4}{3}$$

that is

$$0 = \frac{a}{3} - \frac{4}{3}$$

or $a = 4$ as before.

The examples so far show that the gradient may change when the ordinate is changed. Intercepts on both axes remain the same however the equation is arranged.

(c) $4p = 2q + 5$

Divide through by 4

$$p = \frac{q}{2} + \frac{5}{4}$$

gradient is 1/2, p intercept is 5/4.

To find the q-axis intercept put $p = 0$ to give

$$0 = \frac{q}{2} + \frac{5}{4}$$

that is

$$-\frac{q}{2} = \frac{5}{4}$$

or

$$q = -\frac{5}{2}$$

(d) $4p = 2q + 5$

Subtract 5 from both sides, divide through by 2 and rearrange to give

$$q = 2p - \frac{5}{2}$$

gradient is 2, q-axis intercept is $-5/2$.

When $q = 0$

$$0 = 2p - \frac{5}{2}$$

that is $p = 5/4$, thus p intercept is 5/4 as before.

In general for the equation $y = mx + c$ the intercept on the y axis (at $x = 0$) is c. Now put $y = 0$ to give

$$0 = mx + c$$

that is

$$-mx = c$$

and

$$x = -\frac{c}{m}$$

The intercept on the x axis (at $y = 0$) is thus $-c/m$. These intercepts remain the same which ever variable is plotted as ordinate. However the gradient of the graph changes as follows: the gradient of $y = mx + c$ is m; rearrange to give

$$mx = y - c$$

that is

$$x = \frac{y}{m} - \frac{c}{m}$$

and the gradient with x taken as ordinate is $1/m$, that is the reciprocal of m. Note that generally y is the ordinate and x the abscissa but with other less often-used variables the ordinate taken must be stated.

Exercise 5.1

(1) Determine the gradient of the graphs of the following equations when y is plotted as ordinate

(a) $5y - 3x = 7$

(b) $7 - 2y = 3x + 5$

(c) $7(x + y) = 35$

(d) $\dfrac{1}{x - y} = \dfrac{1}{3x + y}$

(e) $\dfrac{2}{5}x = 3y + \dfrac{7}{5}$

(f) $12x = 18y$

(2) Each section of this question gives two points on a straight line graph. Determine the gradient in each case.

(a) $(4, 3), (7, 2)$

(b) $(-4, 6), (5, -6)$

(c) $(1, 1), (-1, -1)$

(d) $\left(\dfrac{4}{3}, -\dfrac{7}{9}\right)$, $\left(\dfrac{5}{6}, \dfrac{2}{9}\right)$

(e) $\left(\dfrac{1}{2}, 4\right)$, $\left(3, \dfrac{-7}{2}\right)$

(f) $(-4, -10), (-10, -14)$

(3) Find without plotting the graphs the intercept on the y axis when x is zero of the graphs of the following functions

(a) $4y = 3x - 7$

(b) $2y + 5x = 8$

(c) $\dfrac{3y + 2x}{8} = 2$

(d) $x = 7 - 3y$

(e) $5(x - y) = 3(x + y)$

(f) $\dfrac{3}{x + y} = \dfrac{5}{x - y}$

(4) Taking the origin as (0, 0) find the intercepts on both axes and the gradients
of the graphs of the following functions

(a) $3a = b + 8$

(b) $4p + q = 7$

(c) $x + y = 5(x - y)$

(d) $5m + 2n = 2$

(e) $\dfrac{a}{3} = \dfrac{b - 5}{4}$

(f) $\dfrac{1}{a + b} = \dfrac{4}{2a - b}$

(5) Graphs of the following functions are drawn on the same axes. State (i) which
graphs are parallel; (ii) which graphs pass through the origin (0, 0); (iii) which
graphs cut one another at the same point on the y axis.

function 1 $4y = 3 - 2x$
function 2 $8y + 2x = 6$
function 3 $4y + 5x = 6y - 7x$
function 4 $y + \tfrac{1}{2}x = 5$

Deducing the equation of a straight-line graph

As was stated at the beginning of this chapter it is often possible to deduce the
equation relating two variables from the shape of a graph plotting the values of
one variable against the other. This is particularly straightforward in the case of
a straight-line graph, the relationship between the variables then being of the
linear form $y = mx + c$ where y and x are the variables and if y is plotted as
ordinate, m is the gradient and c the intercept on the y axis when x is zero.

In problems where deduction of an equation from a graph is required the
graph is invariably obtained by experimental observation, that is in a laboratory
or workshop. In such observation errors inevitably occur due partly to
instruments or meters and partly to reading-error on the part of the observer.
Consequently in cases where it appears that the equation is probably linear not
all the given points will lie exactly on a straight line. Since the graph must first
be drawn before the gradient and intercept can be determined it is advisable to
place it in such a way that as many points lie above the line as lie below it. In
this way the overall error in deduction is reduced since there is approximately as
much error in one direction as in the other, that is the error has been averaged
out. Occasionally in practice one or more points are obtained which appear a
considerable distance from any graph drawn to fit the remaining points. In this
case it is more than likely that the observation of such a point is at fault. It is
important to realise that whereas, as stated earlier, only two points are required
to establish a straight-line graph *if the equation is known and is linear,* as many
points as can possibly be obtained are necessary when attempting to deduce an
equation from a graph. Often a graph may be linear or approximately linear only
over a part of its length. In this book we shall restrict ourselves to linear graphs
but it is as well to appreciate these general points at the outset.

The general technique used in obtaining the equation will be shown in examples. It consists of choosing the scales on each axis, locating the points and then placing the line in the best position to minimise error as explained earlier. The gradient is then obtained by measuring the slope of the line, and the intercept on the ordinate axis when the abscissa is zero, is determined either by reading it directly or if this is not possible, by reading the values of the variables being plotted at a point on the graph and inserting these values into the equation —giving a linear equation with one unknown, the unknown being the required intercept.

The choice of scales when drawing the graph, that is how many length units are taken to represent one unit of the quantity in which the variable is measured (volts, amps, ohms, etc.) is important. The scale should be such that the given part of the graph uses as much as possible of the available graph paper, that is the scales are as expanded as possible. This makes placing points easier and in particular helps considerably when reading values off the graph for gradient and intercepts determination. Occasionally the best choice of scale means that one or both variables being plotted will not be zero at the point where the axes cross, that is the origin will not be $y = 0$, $x = 0$, for a graph plotting y against x. This only happens when the variable concerned does not change polarity—go from positive to negative—if it does the variable will be zero at the origin. It must be remembered when determining c in the general equation $y = mx + c$ that c is the intercept on the ordinate axis only when the abscissa is zero. Study the following examples carefully.

Example 5.4

The voltage drop across a resistor for various currents is as follows

Current (I)	0.2	0.6	1.2	1.6	2.0	2.4	amps
Voltage (V)	10	32	58	80	107	123	volts

Plot the voltage V vertically against current I horizontally. Determine the law relating V and I.

The graph is shown in figure 5.8. In this example both scales begin at zero and the graph when placed so that the points are evenly distributed about it passes through the origin, that is the intercept is zero.

To determine the gradient read off the values of the variables at two suitable points, for example when V is 100 V and 20 V. (Do not use given values as these may not lie on the graph.) At these points the current is 1.95 A and 0.38 A respectively. Thus when V changes by 80 V, the current changes by 1.57 A and the gradient is $80/1.57$, that is 51. The equation is therefore $V = 51\ I$.

An important point to note when measuring gradients is to read the *scales* in all cases. Do not read the length units or divisions on the graph paper, as one length unit or division on the one axis may not represent the same value as one

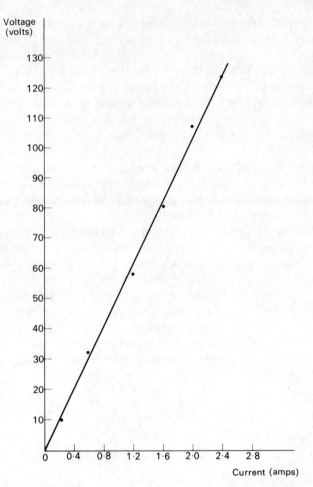

Figure 5.8   Example 5.4

division on the other. In this example for instance, one major division on the V axis represents 10 V whereas the same length unit on the other axis represents 0.4 A. Reading length units or divisions would give a gradient of 2.1 which is incorrect.

Example 5.5

The supply voltage V volts to an electric motor and its speed N rev/s when measured on test were as follows

N	5	10	15	20	25	rev/s
V	55	126	180	237	305	volts

Determine the equation relating N and V making N the subject of the equation.

The graph is shown in figure 5.9. The gradient is (20.6–12)/(250–145), that is 8.6/105 or 0.082 and the intercept is zero. Thus the equation is $N = 0.082\ V$.

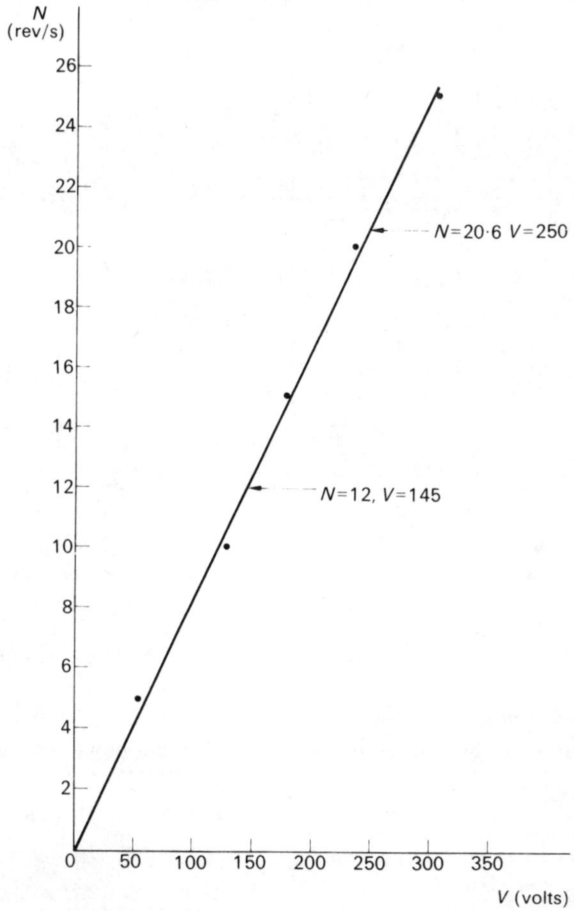

Figure 5.9 Example 5.5

Example 5.6

The output voltage of a power supply V volts and the current taken from it I amps were observed to be as follows

V	30	29	28	27	26	25	volts
I	0.1	0.22	0.3	0.39	0.51	0.6	amps

Determine the equation relating the output voltage and current expressing V in terms of I and hence determine the open circuit or no-load voltage of the power supply.

The graph is shown in figure 5.10. Notice that to obtain maximum accuracy the V scale does not begin at 0. From figure 5.10 when the voltage changes from

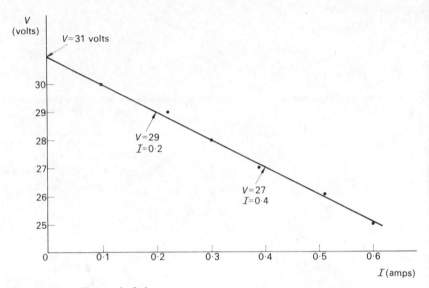

Figure 5.10   Example 5.6

29 V to 27 V the current changes from 0.2 A to 0.4 A. The gradient is thus $(29-27)/(0.2-0.4)$, that is $2/-0.2$ or -10. Note the downward slope of the graph means a negative gradient.

The intercept on the voltage axis is 31 V and at this point the current is zero. The equation is thus $V = -10I + 31$.

The no-load voltage, that is the voltage for zero output-current is the intercept and equals 31 V.

Example 5.7

The equation relating the resistance of a wire R_1 Ω at any temperature t_1 $^\circ$C is believed to be of the form

$$R_1 = R_0(1 + \alpha t_1)$$

where R_0 is the resistance of the wire at 0°C and α is the temperature coefficient of resistance.

The following results were obtained under experimental conditions for a piece of wire having a resistance of 10 Ω at 0°C. Find the value of α for the material used in this piece of wire.

R_1	10.04	10.061	10.079	10.1	10.121	10.139	Ω
t_1	10	15	20	25	30	35	°C

The graph is shown in figure 5.11. Note that to obtain the maximum possible accuracy in locating values of R_1 the scale is expanded as much as possible and does not begin at zero.

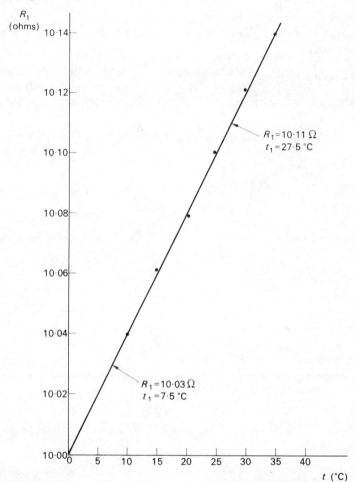

Figure 5.11   *Example 5.7*

From the graph when R_1 = 10.11 Ω, t_1 = 27.5°C and when R_1 = 10.03 Ω, t_1 = 7.5°C, thus the gradient is $(10.11 - 10.03)/(27.5 - 7.5)$, that is 0.004.

Now the equation when expanded is

$$R_1 = \alpha R_0 t_1 + R_0$$

that is the intercept is R_0, given as 10 Ω, and the gradient is αR_0. Thus

$$\alpha R_0 = 0.004$$

and

$$\alpha = 0.0004 \ \Omega/\Omega°C$$

(The units of α are ohms per ohm degree centigrade.)

Example 5.8

The length of a spring l m was measured at various loads of mass m kg giving the following results

l	0.15	0.154	0.161	0.165	0.171	0.176	m
m	0.1	0.11	0.12	0.13	0.14	0.15	kg

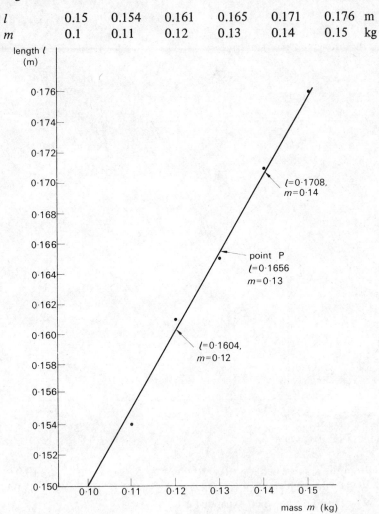

Figure 5.12   Example 5.8

Establish the equation relating *l* in terms of *m* over this range of load and determine the length of the unloaded spring.

To obtain maximum accuracy here it is advisable not to begin either scale at zero since both variables vary over a relatively small range compared to their actual value. Starting the *m* axis for instance at $m = 0$ would mean that the scale from $m = 0$ to $m = 0.1$, which is twice as large as the scale from $m = 0.1$ to $m = 0.15$, would not be used for point location. Similarly the scale from $l = 0$ to $l = 0.15$, which is nearly eight times larger than the scale from $l = 0.15$ to $l = 0.176$, would not be required. Thus to obtain maximum scale expansion the scales begin at $l = 0.15$ and $m = 0.1$. Since *l* is required in terms of *m*, *l* is plotted as ordinate in figure 5.12.

From the graph the gradient is $(0.1708 - 0.1604)/(0.14 - 0.12)$, that is $0.0104/0.02$ or 0.52, and the equation is thus

$$l = 0.52\, m + \text{constant}$$

Since *m* (abscissa) does not equal zero where the *l* (ordinate) axis crosses the *m* axis the intercept of the graph on the *l* axis is not the constant in the above equation. This is obtained by taking values of *l* and *m* from a point on the graph and inserting them into the equation. Thus at point P $l = 0.1656$, $m = 0.13$ and therefore

$$0.1656 = 0.52 \times 0.13 + \text{constant}$$
$$\text{constant} = 0.1656 - 0.52 \times 0.13$$
$$= 0.098$$

and the equation is

$$l = 0.52\, m + 0.098$$

Exercise 5.2

(1) The voltage drop across a resistor for various currents was as follows

Current (*I*)	0.1	0.2	0.3	0.4	0.5	A
Voltage (*V*)	10	21	29	42	48	V

Plot *V* vertically against *I* horizontally and determine the law relating *V* and *I*. What does the gradient of this graph represent practically?

(2) The distance between a body moving with a constant speed and a fixed reference point was noted at various times to give the following results

Distance	60	71	80	89	100	m
Time	1	2	3	4	5	s

Determine the speed of the body and the distance of the body from the reference point at the instant timing commenced.

(3) The speed of a moving body V metres per second is related to the time t seconds by an equation of the form $V = u + at$ where u m/s is the speed when timing begins and a is the acceleration in m/s². The following observation of V and t were made

V	11.4	12.2	13.3	14	15	m/s
t	1	2	3	4	5	s

By plotting a suitable graph find the values of the initial speed and the acceleration for this body.

(4) The resistance of a piece of wire R Ω and the temperature t°C were observed to have the following values

R	1.1	1.106	1.111	1.114	1.12	Ω
t	20	21	22	23	24	°C

Determine the equation relating R and t.

(5) The output voltage of a power supply V volts and the current drawn from it I amps is of the form $V = E - kI$ where E and k are constants. A certain power supply provided 31 V when the current was 0.9 A and 30 V when the current was 0.95 A. Draw a graph showing the variation of output voltage with current and from it determine the values of E and k in this instance. What would be the output voltage when a current of 0.85 A was drawn from the supply?

(6) Observations of the speed N rev/min of a motor and applied voltage V volts were as follows

N	500	550	600	650	700	750	rev/mi
V	49.3	56.1	60.2	64	71	74.8	V

Determine the equation giving N in terms of V.

(7) For the observations of question 6 determine the equation expressing V in terms of N.

(8) Observation of the collector voltage V_c V and collector current I_c mA of a certain transistor gave the following values

I_c	5.04	5.1	5.17	5.23	5.3	mA
V_c	5	6.9	9.1	10.9	12.9	V

By plotting a graph of I_c against V_c determine (a) the equation relating the variables with I_c as subject; (b) the collector current for a collector voltage of 9.2 V.

GRAPHICAL SOLUTION OF SIMULTANEOUS EQUATIONS

As was stated earlier a graph is a means whereby the many pairs of values which satisfy an equation connecting two variable quantities may be shown pictorially. When two different equations connecting the same two variable quantities exist simultaneously there are not so many pairs of values which satisfy both equations at the same time. The number of pairs of values which do so depends in fact on the highest power to which the independent variable is raised. For linear equations this is 1, and there is therefore only 1 pair of values which satisfy two simultaneous linear equations. In chapter 4 we examined the methods by which these values could be found (substitution, elimination, etc.). The use of graphs gives us another method since each graph shows all the values which satisfy the equation, so if the graphs of two equations are drawn using the same axes the point where the graphs cross one another gives the pair of values which satisfies both equations at the same time—because the point of intersection is the only point which lies on both graphs.

The same principle applies to equations of any order, that is containing x^2, x^3, x^4, etc. but as stated above there will in general be more than one pair of values depending on the highest power present and thus more than one point of intersection.

The general technique in solving simultaneous equations using graphs is quite straightforward. Suitable scales are chosen to accommodate the required range of values for both equations. The graphs of the equations are then drawn on the same axes and the solution read off from the point of intersection.

Example 5.9

Solve for x and y the simultaneous equations $y = 3x - 2$ and $3x + y = 5$ (a) by graphical means, (b) by analytical means.

(a) Rearrange the equations to give y as subject, that is $y = 3x - 2$ and $y = 5 - 3x$. Now find three pairs of values for each equation (although two are all that are required to locate a straight line finding three helps to reduce the possibility of error). All three points should fall on the same line, if they do not an error in calculation is likely.

Take

$$x = 0 \quad 1 \quad 2$$

for $y = 3x - 2$

$$y = -2 \quad 1 \quad 4$$

for $y = 5 - 3x$

$$y = 5 \quad 2 \quad -1$$

The graphs are shown in figure 5.13. The point of intersection is $y = 1.5$, $x = 1.16$ and this pair of values satisfies both equations at the same time.

Note that since the point of intersection is not known before drawing the graphs, then unless a range of values is given the point of intersection may lie outside the range chosen. In this case the graphs will have to be redrawn. It is advisable to make a preliminary sketch to determine the approximate point of intersection.

(b) Analytically the solution is determined as follows

$$y = 3x - 2 \tag{5.3}$$
$$y = -3x + 5 \tag{5.4}$$

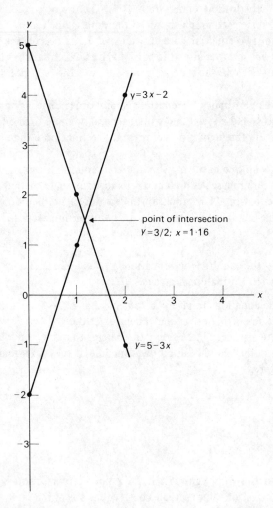

Figure 5.13   Example 5.9

Add equation 5.3 to equation 5.4

$$2y = 3$$

$$y = \frac{3}{2} = 1.5$$

Substitute in equation 5.3

$$\frac{3}{2} = 3x - 2$$

thus

$$x = \frac{1}{3}\left(\frac{3}{2} + 2\right)$$

$$= \frac{7}{6} = 1.166 \ (1.67 \text{ to 2 places})$$

Check in equation 5.4: LHS is 3/2. RHS is

$$-\frac{21}{6} + 5$$

which equals 9/6 or 3/2.

(Check using fractional values if these are available, their accuracy is better than decimal values; for example compare $x = 7/6$ with $x = 1.16$—the final 6 recurs so an approximation must be made.)

6 Geometry

Geometry is the branch of mathematics that deals with points, lines, planes and solids and examines their properties, measurements and mutual relations in space. A study of geometry without regard to its practical use is often tedious and may appear to be without purpose. However engineering students should appreciate that a basic knowledge of the subject is essential and is in constant use in all branches of engineering, from the research and design departments of industry to the shop floor where the final product—whatever it may be—is manufactured.

DEFINITIONS

A *straight line* is a mark indicating the shortest distance between two points. In geometry the points are usually represented by letters and the line by combining the letters of the points joined. Thus in figure 6.1a the lines shown are referred to as AB and BC, their point of meeting being B. Since only two points are needed to define a straight line it is not necessary to refer to any such line by more than two letters.

A *plane surface* is one which wholly contains every straight line joining any two points lying on it. Thus the page on which figure 6.1 is printed is a plane surface when lying flat but may not be so when being turned—a book page usually curves on turning. In diagrams any surface may be represented by the line which is seen when viewing one edge and thus a plane surface will then be represented by a straight line.

The space between two lines or plane surfaces that meet is called an *angle*. An angle in geometry is usually referred to either by the letters referring to the lines (or plane surfaces) which make it or by the letter referring to the point of meeting of the lines or surfaces. Thus in figure 6.1a the angle between lines **AB** and **BC** may be referred to either as angle ABC or angle B. When three letters are used the middle letter refers to the point of meeting of the lines. In practice the word angle is often replaced by the symbol ∠ before the letters or by the symbol ^ placed over the letter referring to the point of meeting. Angle ABC may then be written as ∠ABC or A$\hat{B}$C, ∠B or $\hat{B}$.

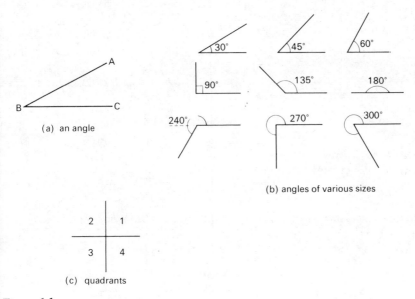

(a) an angle

(b) angles of various sizes

(c) quadrants

Figure 6.1

If a line is rotated about one of its ends, that is if one end is fixed and the other turned then the total angle turned through when the line has made one complete revolution, so that it lies back in its starting place, is measured as 360 *degrees* or 2π *radians*, where π (Greek letter pi) is a constant and equal to 3.1428 to four decimal places. Thus one radian is equal to 360/2π, that is 57.3 degrees. Each degree may be sub-divided into sixty divisions called *minutes* and each minute may be further divided into sixty divisions called *seconds*. The symbols for degree, minute and second as geometrical units are °, ′ and ″ respectively. Thus an angle of 43 degrees 10 minutes 2 seconds could be written as 43° 10′ 2″. The abbreviation for radian is rad. Thus 360° = 2π rad or 1 rad = 57.3°.

Angles of 30°, 45°, 60°, 90°, 135°, 180°, 240°, 270° and 300° are shown in figure 6.1b. Notice the method of marking these angles. An angle of 90° is called a right angle and is, for example, the angle between the horizontal and the vertical. If a total angle of 360° is divided into four such right angles by drawing a vertical and horizontal axis as shown in figure 6.1c each right angle is called a *quadrant*, each quadrant being numbered as shown. Thus the 45° angle shown in the figure lies in the first quadrant, the 240° angle lies in the third quadrant and so on. This point will be made use of in the next chapter on trigonometry. Notice from figure 6.1b that an angle of 180° means that the lines making the angle lie in the same straight line.

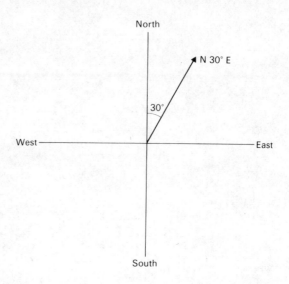

Figure 6.2   Bearing

Two lines lying at right angles are used in navigation to indicate bearing or direction. One is drawn to show the north–south direction and a second to show the east–west direction. A direction or bearing such as that shown in figure 6.2 may then be referred to as N30°E as shown, the first letter indicating the reference direction, the second showing towards which direction the line showing the bearing is moved to create the angle of bearing. (The particular bearing shown could also be referred to as E60°N but the first method is more commonly used.)

Figure 6.3 shows various shapes made up by the meeting of three or more lines. Any shape having a surface totally enclosed by three lines is called a triangle, by four lines is called a quadrangle or quadrilateral and by more than four lines is usually referred to as a polygon.* Special names are given to some of these shapes.

---

*Strictly speaking a polygon is any shape and includes triangles and quadrangles. The word means 'many angles'.

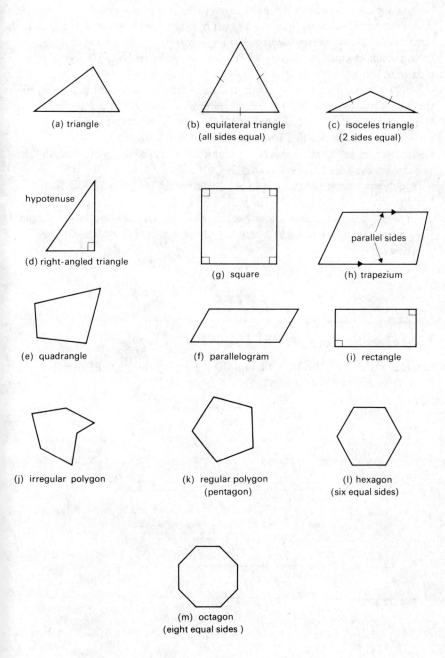

Figure 6.3   Geometrical shapes

A triangle having one of its angles equal to 90° is called a *right-angled triangle*. A triangle with two of its three sides equal in length (or two of its three angles equal) is called an *isosceles triangle*. A triangle with three sides equal in length (or three angles equal in magnitude) is called an *equilateral triangle*. (See figures 6.3a to 6.3d.)

Any two lines drawn so that their distance apart, measured at right angles to the lines, remains constant, that is they never meet, are called *parallel lines*. A quadrangle with one set of parallel sides is called a *trapezium* and with two sets of parallel sides is called a *parallelogram*. A parallelogram having all its angles right angles is called a *rectangle* and if the sides are all equal in length it is called a *square*. (See figures 6.3e to 6.3i.)

A polygon having unequal angles is called *irregular* (figure 6.3j) and one having equal angles is called *regular* (figure 6.3k). Occasionally special names are given to polygons, regular or otherwise, denoting the number of sides—pentagon (five sides), hexagon (six sides), octagon (eight sides), and so on. (See figures 6.3l and 6.3m.)

Angles associated with parallel lines

Consider any two parallel lines AB and CD cut by any third line EF at points X on AB and Y on CD as shown in figure 6.4.

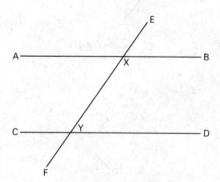

Figure 6.4

The following relationships are true

corresponding angles	$\angle EXA$	$=$	$\angle XYC$
	$\angle EXB$	$=$	$\angle XYD$
	$\angle AXY$	$=$	$\angle CYF$
	$\angle BXY$	$=$	$\angle DYF$
vertically opposite angles	$\angle EXA$	$=$	$\angle BXY$
	$\angle EXB$	$=$	$\angle AXY$
	$\angle XYC$	$=$	$\angle DYF$
	$\angle XYD$	$=$	$\angle CYF$
alternate angles	$\angle AXY$	$=$	$\angle XYD$
	$\angle BXY$	$=$	$\angle XCY$

supplementary angles	$\angle EXA$	$+$	$\angle EXB$	$=$	$180°$
	$\angle AXY$	$+$	$\angle BXY$	$=$	$180°$
	$\angle XYC$	$+$	$\angle XYD$	$=$	$180°$
	$\angle CYF$	$+$	$\angle DYF$	$=$	$180°$

Example 6.1

In figure 6.4 $\angle BXY = 2\angle AXY$. Find all eight angles in the figure.

Since $\angle BXY + \angle AXY = 180°$ (supplementary angles)
then

$$3\angle AXY = 180°$$
$$A\hat{X}Y = 60°$$

and

$$B\hat{X}Y = 120°$$

Therefore

$$E\hat{X}A = B\hat{X}Y = 120°$$

and

$$E\hat{X}B = A\hat{X}Y = 60°$$

also

$$X\hat{Y}C = D\hat{Y}F = 120°$$

and

$$C\hat{Y}F = X\hat{Y}D = 60°$$

from the relationships given above.

PROPERTIES OF TRIANGLES

Sum of interior angles

Consider any triangle XYZ, YZ lying in line CD and line AB drawn parallel to CD and containing X as shown in figure 6.5.

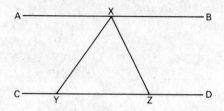

Figure 6.5

From relationships already established

$$A\hat{X}Y = X\hat{Y}Z \quad \text{(alternate angles)}$$
$$B\hat{X}Z = X\hat{Z}Y \quad \text{(alternate angles)}$$

Now

$$A\hat{X}Y + Y\hat{X}Z + B\hat{X}Z = 180° \quad \text{(supplementary angles)}$$

thus

$$X\hat{Y}Z + Y\hat{X}Z + X\hat{Z}Y = 180°$$

that is the sum of the interior angles of any triangle equals 180°.

Exterior angles

Consider any triangle XYZ with ZY continued to any point P as in figure 6.6. Angle XYP is called an exterior angle of the triangle. (Similarly YX could be continued to, say, Q to give exterior angle QXZ as shown or XZ could be continued to R to give exterior angle YZR.)

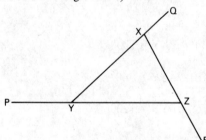

Figure 6.6

Now

$$P\hat{Y}X + X\hat{Y}Z = 180° \quad \text{(supplementary angles)}$$

and

$$X\hat{Y}Z + Y\hat{X}Z + X\hat{Z}Y = 180° \quad \text{(interior angles of a triangle)}$$

thus

$$P\hat{Y}X = Y\hat{X}Z + X\hat{Z}Y$$

that is the exterior angle of a triangle is equal to the sum of the two interior opposite angles.

Example 6.2

In figure 6.7 $A\hat{C}B = 120°$, $A\hat{D}E = 110°$. Find $C\hat{A}D$.

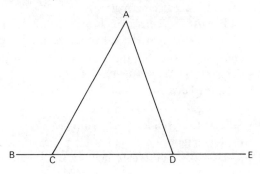

Figure 6.7

$$A\hat{C}B = 120° = C\hat{A}D + A\hat{D}C \quad \text{(interior opposite angles)}$$

but

$$A\hat{D}C = 180 - A\hat{D}E \quad \text{(supplementary angles)}$$
$$= 180 - 110$$
$$= 70°$$

thus

$$120 = 70 + C\hat{A}D$$

and

$$C\hat{A}D = 50°$$

Similar and congruent triangles

If two or more triangles have the same shape, that is corresponding angles in each are equal, they are said to be *similar*. If they have the same shape *and* the same size they are said to be *congruent*. This is illustrated in figure 6.8. In the following discussion the symbol Δ means 'triangle'.

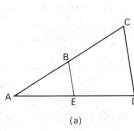

(a)   (b)

Figure 6.8

In figure 6.8a $\triangle$ABE and $\triangle$ACD are similar if line BE is parallel to line CD. For the two triangles

$$B\hat{A}E = C\hat{A}D \quad \text{(same angle)}$$
$$A\hat{B}E = A\hat{C}D \quad \text{(corresponding angles; BE, CD parallel)}$$
$$B\hat{E}A = C\hat{D}A \quad \text{(corresponding angles; BE, CD parallel)}$$

Thus the corresponding angles (but not the sides) in each triangle are the same.

In figure 6.8b, a square ABCD is divided into two triangles $\triangle$ABD and $\triangle$BDC by a line BD (called a *diagonal*). Here for the two triangles

$$AB = DC \quad \text{(sides of a square)}$$
$$BC = AD \quad \text{(sides of a square)}$$
BD is common
$$A\hat{B}D = B\hat{D}C \quad \text{(alternate angles; AB, DC parallel)}$$
$$A\hat{D}B = D\hat{B}C \quad \text{(alternate angles; AD, BC parallel)}$$
$$B\hat{A}D = B\hat{C}D = 90°$$

Thus the two triangles have three sides and three angles the same and are congruent.

In fact, congruency requires only three conditions, these being for the two triangles compared

three sides equal (SSS)
two sides and the contained angle equal (SAS)
two angles and corresponding side equal (AAS)
right angle, side opposite right angle and one other side equal (RHS)

The abbreviations shown in parentheses are an aid to memory, the letters RHS in the last set of conditions standing for right angle, *hypotenuse* and side. The special name hypotenuse is given to the side in a triangle opposite to a right angle. The conditions are illustrated in figure 6.9.

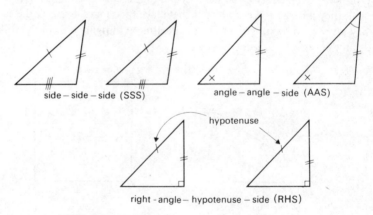

Figure 6.9   Conditions for congruency

Isosceles and equilateral triangles

Figure 6.10a shows an isosceles triangle with sides **AB** and **AC** equal in length. If a line AD at right angles to BC is drawn, cutting BC at D we now have two triangles △BAD and △DAC.

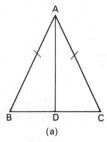

Figure 6.10

(a)   (b)

Since in these triangles

$$AB = AC \quad \text{(given)}$$
$$AD \text{ is common}$$
$$A\hat{D}B = A\hat{D}C = 90°$$

the triangles are congruent and thus

$$A\hat{B}D = A\hat{C}D$$
$$BD = DC$$
$$B\hat{A}D = D\hat{A}C$$

For an isosceles triangle therefore the angles opposite the equal sides are equal and a line drawn from the point of meeting of the equal sides to the third side at right angles to it bisects (divides into two equal parts) both the angle between the equal sides and the third side.

Figure 6.10b shows an equilateral triangle ABC having AB = BC = CA. It follows from above that

$$A\hat{B}C = B\hat{C}A$$

and

$$B\hat{C}A = C\hat{A}B$$

so that all the internal angles are equal and thus must each be 60° (since their sum is 180°).

Example 6.3

In figure 6.11 AB = BC and DE = EF. Calculate $B\hat{G}E$ if $A\hat{B}C = 50°$ and $D\hat{E}F = 70°$.

Now

$$B\hat{G}E = D\hat{G}C \quad \text{(vertically opposite)}$$

and $D\hat{G}C$ lies in △DGC containing two angles $G\hat{D}C$ and $G\hat{C}D$ which can be found as follows

in △ABC

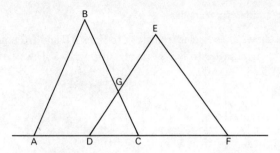

Figure 6.11   Example 6.3

$$B\hat{A}C + A\hat{B}C + B\hat{C}A = 180°$$

and

$$A\hat{B}C = 50° \text{(given)}$$
$$B\hat{A}C = B\hat{C}A \text{(isosceles triangle)}$$

so that

$$2B\hat{C}A = 180° - 50°$$

thus

$$B\hat{C}A = G\hat{C}D = 65°$$

Similarly in △DEF

$$E\hat{D}F = G\hat{D}C = \tfrac{1}{2}(180 - 70)$$

since

$$D\hat{E}F = 70° \text{ and } E\hat{D}F = E\hat{F}D$$

so that

$$G\hat{D}C = 55°$$

therefore

$$D\hat{G}C = 180 - G\hat{D}C - G\hat{C}D$$
$$= 180 - 55 - 15$$
$$= 110°$$

Right-angled triangles

One of the most widely used theorems concerned with right-angled triangles is
Pythagoras' theorem. For the triangle ABC in figure 6.12, in which ∠ABC is
the right angle, Pythagoras' theorem states

$$AC^2 = AB^2 + BC^2$$

The side opposite the right angle in a right-angled triangle is called the
hypotenuse so that in general terms for any such triangle the theorem states

(length of hypotenuse)² = sum of squares of lengths of remaining sides

Thus, if the lengths of any two sides of a right-angled triangle are known, the
length of the third side may be found.

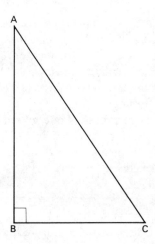

Figure 6.12

Example 6.4

A ladder 5 m long rests against a wall at a point 4 m above the ground. Determine the distance between the foot of the ladder and the bottom of the wall.

Using figure 6.12 in which AC represents the ladder, that is AC = 5 m, AB represents the wall and AB = 4 m so BC is the required distance.

$$BC^2 = AC^2 - AB^2$$
$$= 25 - 16$$
$$= 9$$

Thus BC = 3 m.

Example 6.5

A flagpole 12 m high is supported at its top by four guy-ropes each anchored a distance of 5 m from the base of the pole. Calculate the total length of rope required.

Using figure 6.12 again, AB represents the flagpole and equals 12 m, BC represents the distance between pole base and guy-rope anchor and equals 5 m. AC is the length of rope and 4AC the total length required.

$$AC^2 = AB^2 + BC^2$$
$$= 12^2 + 5^2$$
$$= 144 + 25$$
$$= 169$$
$$AC = 13$$
$$4AC = 52$$

therefore total length of guy-rope is 52 m.

Examples 6.4 and 6.5 used two right-angled triangles having sides the lengths of which were integers, that is 3, 4 and 5 (5 being the hypotenuse) and 5, 12 and 13 (13 being the hypotenuse). These two sets of figures are useful to remember since they invariably indicate a right-angled triangle. Bearing in mind similar triangle definitions this also applies to triangles having sides in the ratio of 3 : 4 : 5, or 5 : 12 : 13; for example 6, 8 and 10; 9, 12 and 15, etc.; or 10, 24 and 26; 15, 36 and 39, etc. Other ratios of integers indicating right-angled triangles (when they refer to side lengths) are 7 : 24 : 25 and 8 : 15 : 17 and their multiples. Pythagoras' theorem of course applies to all right-angled triangles whether or not their side lengths are integers.

Exercise 6.1

(1) It is desired to connect a remote monitoring-station to a central control-room by underground cable. The distance and bearing of the station from a certain reference point is 120 km due north, the distance and bearing of the control-room from the same point is 50 km due east. Calculate the shortest run of cable required.

(2) A telephone pole 6 m high situated 150 m from the subscriber's house is to be connected to the house by a wire running from the top of the pole to a point of entry at the house, situated 4 m from the ground. Assuming both pole and house are on level ground calculate the length of wire required.

(3) Two taut supporting-ropes fixed to the top of a pylon 50 m high have their other ends in level ground either side of the pylon, the pylon base and the rope ends lying in the same straight line. The ground fixing-points are 15 m apart, one of them being 7 m from the pylon base. Calculate the length of the ropes.

(4) Two parallel lines AB and CD are cut by two other lines XY and ZY, line XY cutting AB at X and line ZY cutting CD at Z. Lines XY and ZY meet at Y. If $A\hat{X}Y = 25°$ and $D\hat{Z}Y = 145°$ calculate $X\hat{Y}Z$.

(5) Two triangles ABC and BCD are joined together along the line BC. If $A\hat{B}C = 35°$, $B\hat{A}C$ is a right angle and triangle BCD is equilateral calculate $A\hat{C}D$.

(6) If AB were parallel to DE and BC parallel to EF in figure 6.11 show that triangles ABC and DEF would be similar. What extra condition would make them congruent?

(7) In figure 6.7 if $C\hat{A}D = 40°$ and $B\hat{C}A = 50°$ find $A\hat{D}E$.

(8) A ladder 7.5 m long rests against a wall at a point 6 m above the ground. Determine the distance between the foot of the ladder and the bottom of the wall.

PROPERTIES OF QUADRANGLES AND OTHER POLYGONS

As was stated earlier a three-sided figure is called a triangle and a four-sided figure a quadrangle, the word polygon usually being reserved for figures having more than four sides. Strictly speaking any shape comes under the general heading 'polygon'. Some of the more important properties of polygons, other than triangles, will now be examined.

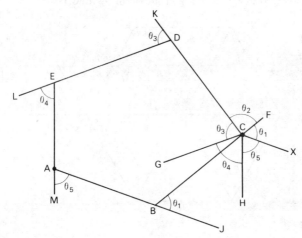

Figure 6.13

The exterior angles of any polygon when added always equal 360°. Figure 6.13 shows an irregular polygon with five sides (pentagon) AB, BC, CD, DE and EA. The exterior angles are $\theta_1, \theta_2, \theta_3, \theta_4$ and θ_5 as shown. If now a line CX is drawn parallel to AB then

$$F\hat{C}X = C\hat{B}J = \theta_1 \quad \text{(corresponding angles)}$$

thus

$$D\hat{C}X = \theta_1 + \theta_2$$

Now draw a line CG parallel to DE so that

$$D\hat{C}G = K\hat{D}E = \theta_3 \quad \text{(corresponding angles)}$$

and therefore

$$D\hat{C}X + D\hat{C}G = \theta_1 + \theta_2 + \theta_3$$

Now draw a line CH parallel to EA so that

$$G\hat{C}H = L\hat{E}A = \theta_4 \quad \text{(corresponding angles)}$$

so that

$$D\hat{C}X + D\hat{C}G + G\hat{C}H = \theta_1 + \theta_2 + \theta_3 + \theta_4$$

Since CX is parallel to AB then $X\hat{C}H = B\hat{A}M$ and $B\hat{A}M = \theta_5$ so that

$$X\hat{C}F + F\hat{C}D + D\hat{C}G + G\hat{C}H + X\hat{C}H = \theta_1 + \theta_2 + \theta_3 + \theta_4 + \theta_5$$

But the sum of these angles is 360° (one complete revolution) and thus the sum of the polygon's exterior angles is 360° as stated. For a regular polygon (having sides of equal length) the exterior angles are equal and since there is one exterior angle for each side of the polygon the value of each exterior angle = 360°/*n* where *n* is the number of sides.

Example 6.6

Calculate $A\hat{B}D$ in the regular polygon shown in figure 6.14.

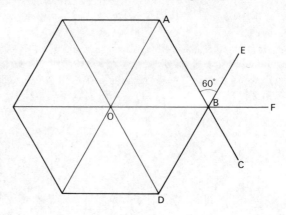

Figure 6.14

Now

$$A\hat{B}E = \frac{360°}{6} \text{ (exterior angles)}$$
$$= 60°$$

and

$$A\hat{B}D = 180° - A\hat{B}E$$
$$= 180° - 60°$$
$$= 120°$$

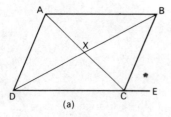 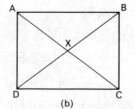 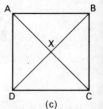

(a)   (b)   (c)

Figure 6.15   Diagonals

Lines drawn between corners in a geometrical figure, that is between points of intersection of sides, are usually referred to as *diagonals*. Figure 6.15 shows the diagonals in a parallelogram, rectangle and square. In these figures

$$A\hat{X}B = D\hat{X}C \quad \text{(vertically opposite)}$$
$$A\hat{B}D = B\hat{D}C \quad \text{(alternate angles)}$$
$$AB = CD \quad \text{(given)}$$

Thus the triangles AXB, DXC are congruent and therefore BX = XD and AX = XC (corresponding sides). The diagonals of these figures thus bisect one another at point X.

It could also be shown that triangles AXD and BXC are congruent and in the case of the square (a regular four-sided polygon) triangles ABX, BXC, CXD and AXD are not only congruent but equilateral. Similarly with figure 6.14, the regular hexagon there is divided into six equilateral triangles by the three diagonals shown.

Example 6.7

If side DC in figure 6.15a is continued to any point E, $B\hat{C}E = 35°$ and BC = CD. Find $A\hat{X}B$.

Now

$$A\hat{B}C = B\hat{C}E = 35° \quad \text{(alternate angles)}$$

and in $\triangle ABC$, since AB = BC (isosceles triangle)

$$B\hat{A}C = B\hat{C}A = \tfrac{1}{2}(180 - A\hat{B}C)$$
$$= 72.5°$$

$\triangle ABD$ and $\triangle BCD$ are congruent (SSS), therefore $A\hat{B}D = D\hat{B}C$, and since

$$A\hat{B}D + D\hat{B}C = 35°$$
$$A\hat{B}D = 17.5°$$

therefore

$$A\hat{X}B = 180 - A\hat{B}D - B\hat{A}C$$
$$= 180 - 17.5 - 72.5$$
$$= 90°$$

PROPERTIES OF CIRCLES

If any arm OX is rotated about the point O, with O fixed, the shape enclosed by the line traced out by X when OX has moved through 360° is called a *circle*. A circle is thus any shape having a boundary which is situated the same distance from a fixed point at all points along the boundary. The fixed point O in the figure is the *centre* of the circle; the distance of the boundary from the centre OX is the *radius* of the circle. The length of the boundary is called the *circumference* of the circle and if any radius is continued to meet the circumference on both sides of the centre (ZX in the figure) the distance between the points of intersection of the continued radius and the circumference is called the circle *diameter.* Clearly the diameter is equal in length to twice the radius.

For all circles the ratio of the circumference length to the length of the diameter is constant and is denoted by the Greek symbol π. This constant has the value 3.1416 to four places of decimals and may be approximated as required. As an improper fraction π may be written as 22/7 for most purposes. Thus

$$\frac{\text{circumference}}{\text{diameter}} = \pi$$

and

$$\text{circumference} = \pi \times \text{diameter}$$

or $2\pi \times$ radius.

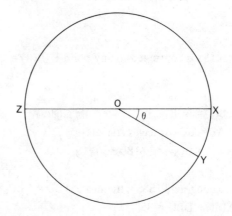

Figure 6.16   Properties of a circle

Any part of a circle circumference is referred to as an *arc.* In figure 6.16 XY is an arc of the circle shown. If radii OX and OY are drawn the angle XOY is said to be *subtended* by the arc XY. The angle subtended at the centre by an arc equal to the radius, that is XY = OX, is defined as one *radian.* Clearly if the arc XY is increased until it becomes the circumference the angle XOY then equals 360°. Now the circumference is equal to $2\pi \times$ radius, then since an arc of length 1 radius subtends an angle of 1 radian, an arc of length $2\pi \times$ radius subtends an angle of 2π radians.
Thus

$$360° = 2\pi \text{ rad}$$

and

$$1 \text{ radian} = 57.3°$$

as stated earlier.

It follows that if an arc of 1 radius length r subtends an angle of 1 radian, then an arc of any length l subtends an angle l/r radians. If this angle is denoted by θ as in figure 6.16 then

$$\theta = \frac{l}{r}$$

or

$$l = r\theta$$

where θ is in radians. Thus the length of any arc of a circle is equal to the radius multiplied by the angle subtended by the arc at the centre, the angle being expressed in radians (not degrees).

Example 6.8

The diameters of two gear wheels connected together by a chain drive are 0.2 m and 0.35 m respectively. Calculate (a) the speed of the smaller wheel in rev/min; (b) the linear speed of one of the chain links when the larger of the two wheels is rotating at 1000 rev/min.

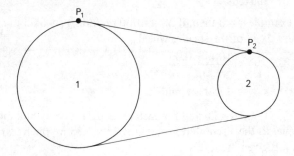

Figure 6.17   Example 6.8

A drawing of the two wheels is shown in figure 6.17. A chain drive is one using connected links meshing with specially designed teeth on each wheel, such that there is no slip when one wheel is used to drive the other. An example is the drive used on a bicycle. When the wheels are of different diameters one will travel faster or slower than the other depending on whether its diameter is smaller or larger. This is shown by considering points P_1 and P_2 which are fixed on the circumferences of the wheels as indicated in the figure. When a wheel turns through one revolution the fixed point on that wheel moves a distance equal to the circumference of the wheel on which it is situated. Thus when wheel 1 turns through one revolution point P_1 moves through a distance equal to $2\pi r_1$, where r_1 is the radius of wheel 1. Since the two wheels are connected by a chain which does not slip, point P_2 will also move through the same distance. Now for one revolution of wheel 2 point P_2 moves through $2\pi r_2$, where r_2 is the radius of wheel 2, that is through a distance equal to the circumference of wheel 2. Thus if P_2 moves a distance of $2\pi r_1$ then wheel 2 has turned through $2\pi r_1/2\pi r_2$ revolutions, that is r_1/r_2 revolutions. So that for one revolution of wheel 1, wheel 2 moves through r_1/r_2 revolutions.

For a speed of N_1 rev/min for wheel 1 then the speed of wheel 2, N_2 say, will equal $N_1 r_1/r_2$, that is

$$\frac{N_2}{N_1} = \frac{r_1}{r_2}$$

The respective speeds of the wheels are thus inversely proportional to their radii all other factors being constant, that is since

$$N_2 = N_1 \frac{r_1}{r_2}$$

then

$$N_2 \propto \frac{1}{r_2}$$

if N_1 and r_1 are constant.

(a) For the example given then, if $N_1 = 1000$ rev/min, $r_1 = 0.35$ m and $r_2 = 0.2$ m, the speed of the smaller wheel

$$N_2 = \frac{1000 \times 0.35}{0.2}$$

$$= 1750 \text{ rev/min}$$

(b) Since $N_1 = 1000$ rev/min and for each revolution a chain link moves through a distance equal to the circumference, that is $2\pi \times 0.35$ m, the linear speed of any chain link is given by

$$2\pi \times 0.35 \times 1000 \text{ m/min}$$

that is 2200 m/min.

Example 6.9

The radius of the tyres of a car is 0.22 m. Calculate the wheel turning-speed in revolutions per second when the car is travelling at 40 km/h.

In one hour the car moves 40×10^3 m then in one second the car moves $40 \times 10^3/3600$ m.

Now for every revolution of the car wheel the car moves a distance of $2 \times \pi \times$ wheel radius which in this case is $2\pi \times 0.22$ m. Thus

$$\text{wheel turning-speed} = \frac{40 \times 10^3}{3600 \times 2 \times \pi \times 0.22} \text{ rev/s}$$

$$= 8.05 \text{ rev/s}$$

Example 6.10

Three gear-wheels are meshed into one another as shown in figure 6.18.
The diameters of the largest and middle wheels are 0.5 m and 0.1 m respectively.
When the smallest wheel is turned at 1000 rev/min the middle wheel turns at
200 rev/min. Calculate the rotational speed in revolutions per second of the
largest wheel under these conditions, and the diameter of the smallest wheel.

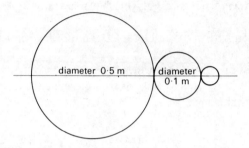

diameter 0·5 m
diameter
0·1 m

Figure 6.18   Example 6.10

Since the ratio of the largest-wheel diameter to the middle-wheel diameter is
0.5 : 0.1, that is 5 : 1, then the ratio of their speeds is 1 : 5, that is the largest
wheel will rotate at 200/5 rev/min. Thus, the rotational speed of the largest
wheel is 200/300 rev/s, that is 0.67 rev/s.

Similarly, since the ratio of smallest-wheel speed to middle-wheel speed is
1000 to 200, that is 5 : 1, the ratio of their diameters is 1 : 5. Thus the
smallest-wheel diameter is 1/5 of 0.1 m, that is 0.02 m.

Exercise 6.2

(1) The diameters of two gear wheels connected together by a chain drive are
0.1 m and 0.2 m respectively. If the larger wheel is rotating at 400 rev/min
calculate the speed of any point on the circumference of the smaller wheel
in cm/s.

(2) A pulley radius 2 cm has a piece of string wound round its circumference
ten times and a mass attached to the end of the string. If the pulley centre is
fixed 400 cm above the ground and the mass is allowed to fall making the pulley
revolve as it does so, determine (a) the distance between the mass and ground
when the string is taut; (b) the number of revolutions of the pulley before this
occurs.

(3) Determine the rotational speed of a gear wheel radius 30 cm drawn by a
chain having a linear velocity of 3 m/s.

(4) The maximum speed allowed for the rim of a certain cast-iron flywheel is 20 m/s. Determine the maximum rotational speed allowed for a flywheel of radius 1.5 m.

(5) A car wheel has a diameter of 0.45 m. Calculate the road speed in km/h when the wheels are rotating at 6 rev/s.

(6) Calculate $B\hat{A}D$ in the regular polygon shown in figure 6.14.

(7) In figure 6.15a $A\hat{X}B = 90°$ and BC = CD. Find $B\hat{C}E$ when $A\hat{B}X = 33°$.

(8) A rectangle of metal ABCD in which AB = 30 and CB = 40 is divided into four triangles by cutting along the diagonals. Determine the lengths of the sides of all the triangles obtained.

AREAS

The word area means a surface measured in square units. These units will be the square of the length unit in whatever system of measurement is being used. For the metric system the units are square kilometres, square metres or square centimetres abbreviated as km^2, m^2 and cm^2 respectively. To illustrate a square unit consider figure 6.19. Part a shows a square of side 1 unit and the area of

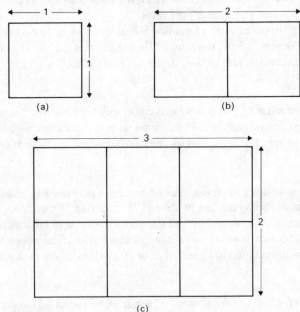

Figure 6.19   Areas

this square by definition is 1 square unit. Part b shows a rectangle of sides 2 units and 1 unit. As shown this figure may be considered to be made up of two squares of side 1 unit and thus the area is 2 square units. Part c shows a rectangle of sides 3 units and 2 units and the figure as a whole is made up of 3 × 2, that is six squares of side 1 unit. The area is thus 6 square units. In general for a rectangle of sides *a* and *b* units the area will be *a* × *b* units and for a square of side *a* the area will be *a* × *a* or a^2 square units.

Example 6.11

Calculate the total surface area of (a) a cube of side 2 m shown in figure 6.20a; (b) a rectangular box of sides 0.5, 0.2 and 0.1 m shown in figure 6.20b.

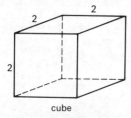 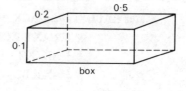

cube   box

Figure 6.20   Example 6.11

(a) The cube has six faces each of area 2 × 2 m. Thus the total surface area is 6 × 2 × 2, that is 24 m².

(b) The box has two faces of area 0.5 × 0.2 m², two faces of area 0.5 × 0.1 m² and two faces of area 0.2 × 0.1 m².

total surface area = (2 × 0.5 × 0.2) + (2 × 0.5 × 0.1) + (2 × 0.2 × 0.1)
= 0.2 + 0.1 + 0.04
= 0.34 m²

Area of triangles

Figure 6.21 shows a triangle ABC in which the angles may have any value. AX is drawn perpendicular to BC, that is at right angles to BC, and is the *height* of the triangle above the *base* line BC. Lines BZ, CY and ZY are drawn to form a rectangle BZYC.

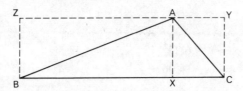

Figure 6.21   Area of a triangle

Since AZ = BX, BZ = AX and AB is common, triangles ABZ and ABX are congruent and have the same surface area. Since the two triangles make up the rectangle ZAXB each has an area equal to half the area of the rectangle.
That is

$$\text{area } \triangle ABZ = \text{area } \triangle ABX$$
$$= \tfrac{1}{2} \times AX \times BX$$

where AX, BX denote the lengths of these lines respectively.

Similarly, since rectangle AYCX is made up of two congruent triangles AYC and ACX

$$\text{area } ACX = \text{area } ACY$$
$$= \tfrac{1}{2} \times AX \times XC$$

Now

$$\text{area } \triangle ABC = \text{area } \triangle ACX + \text{area } \triangle ABX$$
$$= \tfrac{1}{2} \times AX \times XC + \tfrac{1}{2} \times AX \times BX$$
$$= \tfrac{1}{2} AX (XC + BX)$$
$$= \tfrac{1}{2} AX \times BC$$

(since BC = BX + XC)

$$= \tfrac{1}{2} \times \text{height} \times \text{base}$$

This is true for all triangles

Example 6.12

Find the area of the triangle ABC shown in figure 6.21 in which AB = 13, AC = 6.25 and AX = 5.

$$\text{area } \triangle ABC = \tfrac{1}{2} \times BC \times AX$$
$$= \tfrac{1}{2} (BX + XC) \times 5$$

Now

$$BX^2 = AB^2 - AX^2 \quad \text{(Pythagoras)}$$
$$= 13^2 - 5^2$$
$$= 144$$

and

$$BX = 12$$

Similarly

$$XC^2 = AC^2 - AX^2$$
$$= 6.25^2 - 5^2$$
$$= 14.06$$

and

$$XC = 3.75$$

Thus

$$BC = 15.75$$

and

$$\text{area } \triangle ABC = \tfrac{1}{2} \times 15.75 \times 5$$
$$= 39.38 \text{ square units}$$

Example 6.13

A right pyramid is made up of four isosceles triangles each having equal sides 5 m long and a base 6 m long. Determine the total surface area of the pyramid including the base.

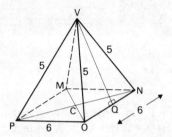

Figure 6.22   Example 6.13

The pyramid is shown in figure 6.22. The word 'right' in the name indicates that the *vertex* of the pyramid, point V shown, lies directly above the geometrical centre of the square base, that is a perpendicular from V to the base passes through the base centre C. The total surface area is the sum of the areas of four isosceles triangles plus the area of the base.

If a line VQ is drawn in one of the triangles VNO at right angles to ON, the line VQ is the height of the triangle and, since $\triangle$VNO is isosceles, bisects the base ON into two equal parts OQ and QN.

Now in $\triangle$VOQ, side VO = 5, OQ = 1/2 × 6 that is 3. VOQ is a right-angled triangle and thus VQ is 4 (3, 4, 5 triangle from Pythagoras' theorem).

$$\text{area } \triangle VON = 2 \times \text{area } \triangle VOQ$$
$$= 2 \times \tfrac{1}{2} \, OQ \times VQ$$
$$= 3 \times 4 \text{ m}^2$$
$$= 12 \text{ m}^2$$
$$\text{area of base} = \text{area of square MNOP}$$
$$= 6 \times 6$$
$$= 36 \text{ m}^2$$

Thus

$$\text{total surface area} = (4 \times 12) + 36$$
$$= 84 \text{ m}^2$$

Example 6.14

Find the area of the parallelogram ABCD shown in figure 6.23 in which AB = 15 cm, BC = 13 cm and the distance between sides AB and CD shown as AY is 12 cm.

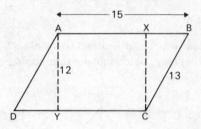

Figure 6.23   Example 6.14

Draw CX parallel to AY. Since AB and CD are parallel CX = AY = 12 cm. Angles $A\hat{D}Y$ and $X\hat{B}C$ are equal and AD = BC so that $\triangle ADY$ and $\triangle XBC$ are congruent.

Total area of parallelogram = 2 × area $\triangle ADY$ + area AXCY

$$= 2 \times \tfrac{1}{2} DY \times AY + AX \times CX$$

Now

$$DY^2 = 13^2 - 12^2 \quad \text{(Pythagoras)}$$
$$= 25$$
$$DY = 5$$

Thus BX = 5 and AX = YC = 10.

Therefore

$$\text{total area required} = 2 \times \tfrac{1}{2} DY \times AY + AX \times CX$$
$$= 2 \times \tfrac{1}{2} \times 5 \times 12 + 10 \times 12$$
$$= 60 + 120$$
$$= 180 \text{ cm}^2$$

Area of a trapezium

As was stated earlier a trapezium is a four-sided figure (a quadrangle) with two sides parallel. Consider any trapezium ABCF as shown in figure 6.24, the perpendicular distance between the parallel lines AB and CF being AE (or BD).

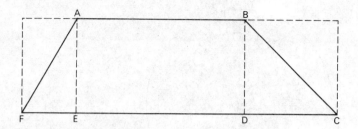

Figure 6.24   Area of a trapezium

$$\text{area} = \text{area } \triangle AEF + \text{area rectangle } ABDE + \text{area } \triangle BDC$$
$$= \tfrac{1}{2} AE \times EF + AE \times AB + \tfrac{1}{2} BD \times DC$$

and since BD = AE (because AB is parallel to CF)

$$\text{area} = \tfrac{1}{2} AE \times EF + AE \times AB + \tfrac{1}{2} AE \times DC$$
$$= \tfrac{1}{2} AE (EF + 2AB + DC)$$

Now

$$EF + AB + DC = EF + ED + DC$$

(since AB = ED)

$$= FC$$

so that

$$\tfrac{1}{2} AE (EF + 2AB + DC) = \tfrac{1}{2} AE (EF + AB + DC + AB)$$
$$= \tfrac{1}{2} AE (FC + AB)$$

that is the area of a trapezium is equal to one-half of the sum of the parallel sides multiplied by the perpendicular distance between them.

Area of a circle

If any circle is subdivided into a very large number of wedge-shaped sectors as shown in figure 6.25 the total circle area is equal to the areas of these sectors added together. If each sector is small enough it may be considered to be a triangle such as OAB, shown in the figure, in which the triangle height OX equals the circle radius and the angle AOB is denoted as θ radians. Now AB, since it forms a very small arc of a circle, is given by

$$AB = r\theta$$

and so

$$\text{area } \triangle OAB = \tfrac{1}{2} OX \times AB$$
$$= \tfrac{1}{2} r \times r\theta$$
$$= \tfrac{1}{2} r^2 \theta$$

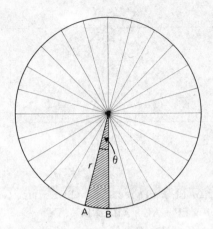

Figure 6.25   Area of a circle

total area of the circle = sum of areas of all sectors such as OAB

$$= \tfrac{1}{2} r^2 \theta_1 + \tfrac{1}{2} r^2 \theta_2 + \tfrac{1}{2} r^2 \theta_3 + \dots$$
$$= \tfrac{1}{2} r^2 (\theta_1 + \theta_2 + \theta_3 + \dots)$$

where $\theta_1, \theta_2, \theta_3$, etc., represent the angles AOB in each sector.

But the sum of these angles is 2π radians by definition, thus

$$\text{circle area} = \tfrac{1}{2} r^2 \times 2\pi$$
$$= \pi r^2$$

or $\pi d^2 / 4$ where d is the diameter.

(This summing process is called *integration* and is a very important mathematical process. It is considered in more detail in volume three of this series.)

Example 6.15

In order to determine the cooling efficiency of a copper conductor it is necessary first to find its surface area. Find the total surface area of a cylindrical conductor of length 0.5 m and radius 0.01 m.

The conductor is shown in figure 6.26a. As indicated a cylinder has a cross-section consisting of a circle of constant size, that is if the cylinder is cut in a plane perpendicular to its length, the resultant shape is always a circle with the same radius.

The surface area of the cylinder ends = 2 × area of one end

$$= 2 \times \pi \times 0.01^2$$
$$= 0.0002\, \pi \text{ m}^2$$

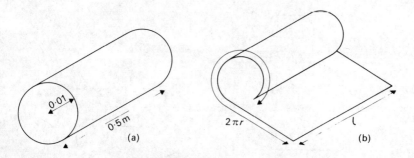

Figure 6.26   Example 6.15–area of a cylinder

The curved surface of any cylinder radius r, length l, is equal to the area of a rectangle of length $2\pi r$ and width l (see figure 6.26b showing the curved surface being 'opened out'), that is $2\pi rl$.
In this case

$$\text{area of curved surface} = 2\pi \times 0.01 \times 0.5$$
$$= 0.01\pi \text{ m}^2$$
$$\text{total conductor area} = 0.0102\pi \text{ m}^2$$
$$= 102\pi \times 10^{-4} \text{ m}^2$$

and since $10^{-4} \text{ m}^2 = 1 \text{ cm}^2$

$$\text{total area} = 102\pi \text{ cm}^2$$
$$= 320 \text{ cm}^2$$

Example 6.16

A transistor heat-sink is of the form and has the dimensions shown in figure 6.27. Calculate the total cooling surface area of the heat sink.

The total surface area is the sum of the areas

$$(2 \times \text{surface A}) + (3 \times \text{surface B}) + (2 \times \text{surface C})$$

Surface A   This surface area is the difference between the area of the outer circle, diameter 13 mm, and the area of the inner circle, diameter 5 mm. That is

$$\text{area of surface A} = \frac{\pi \times 13^2}{4} - \frac{\pi \times 5^2}{4}$$
$$= \frac{144\pi}{4} \text{ mm}^2$$

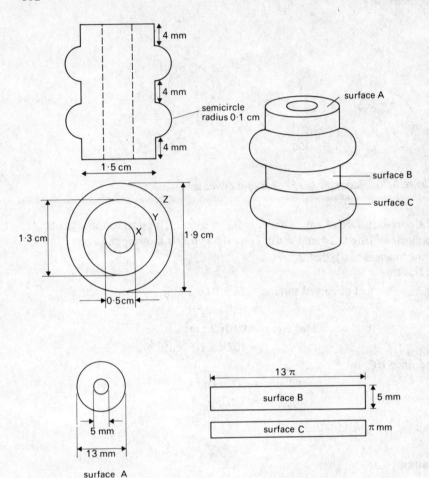

Figure 6.27   Example 6.16

Surface B This surface is the curved surface of a cylinder, that is the same as that of a rectangle of length 13π mm (circumference of outer circle of surface A) and width 4 mm.

$$\text{area of surface B} = 13\pi \times 4$$
$$= 52\pi \text{ mm}^2$$

Surface C When this surface is opened out (see figure 6.27) it is a rectangle of length equal to the circumference of the outer circle of surface A, that is 13π mm, and width equal to one-half the circumference of a circle radius 1 mm, that is $1/2 \times 2\pi$ or π mm.

area of surface $C = 13\pi^2$ mm^2

total surface area $= 2 \times \dfrac{144\pi}{4} + 3 \times 52\pi + 2 \times 13\pi^2$

$\qquad\qquad\qquad = 72\pi + 156\pi + 26\pi^2$ mm^2

$\qquad\qquad\qquad = 973$ mm^2

Exercise 6.3

(1) A cylindrical oil-tank of height 3 m and diameter 1.4 m is to be painted. Calculate the amount of paint required if the average coverage of the paint to be used is 12 m^2/litre.

(2) Determine the surface area of a rectangular tank of dimensions 4 m x 5 m x 2 m.

(3) A certain material disperses heat energy at the rate of 0.13 J/m^2. Determine the energy dispersed by a cooling surface made up of six triangular sections each of them being an equilateral triangle of side 45 cm.

(4) Calculate the total surface area per metre length of a copper conductor of circular cross-section, diameter 12.5 cm.

(5) An air-extraction system contains a box section having a cross-section that is rectangular. The side of the box section is a trapezium. The dimensions of the rectangle are 0.4 m and 0.6 m and of the two parallel sides of the trapezium are 1.4 m and 1.8 m. Sketch a three-dimensional drawing of the box section and calculate the total surface area of the material required to manufacture it. (End areas are not included since the section connects to further sections.)

(6) A case for an electronic power supply is of rectangular cross-section, the dimensions being 20 cm x 15 cm x 10 cm. In each supply three rectangular heat-sinks are required of dimensions 150 mm x 130 mm and each supply also contains a chassis made from a rectangular piece of metal of dimensions 19.5 cm x 14.5 cm. Calculate the total area of metal required for the cases of one hundred of these power supplies.

(7) Calculate the number of circles of diameter 12 cm that can be cut from a rectangle of metal of dimensions 1.2 m x 0.8 m. What is the total area of waste metal?

(8) A transistor heat-sink consists of a cylinder of external diameter 14 mm, internal diameter 5 mm and height 25 mm, to which are fixed six radial fins. Each fin is rectangular and has the dimensions 25 mm × 5 mm × 1 mm, the 25 mm side of each fin being fixed to the cylinder body in a direction along the cylinder axis. Estimate the total area of the cooling surface of the heat-sink.

(9) A metal components drawer consists of an open rectangular box of dimensions 25 cm × 15 cm × 5 cm with dividers to separate the drawer into 15 sub-compartments each of dimensions 5 cm × 5 cm × 5 cm. Calculate (a) the area of material used for the box; (b) the area of material used for the dividers.

(10) An electronic chassis is to be made from a rectangular piece of metal of dimensions 40 cm × 20 cm. Holes of diameters 5, 4, 3 and 2 cm are cut into the chassis as well as a rectangular hole of dimensions 3.5 cm × 7 cm. Calculate the surface area of the chassis when this material has been removed.

VOLUMES

The volume of any body is the amount of space occupied in three dimensions, that is taking into account height, width and depth. The unit of measurement is the cube of the length unit. In the SI system of units this is the cubic metre (m^3)

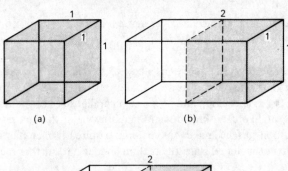

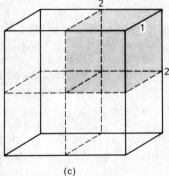

Figure 6.28   Volumes

with its multiples and sub-multiples of cubic kilometre (km^3), cubic centimetre (cm^3 or cc), cubic millimetre (mm^3), etc. Examine figure 6.28 which shows drawings of various bodies. (Note that as with certain previous figures these illustrate the three dimensions of height, width and depth in a two-dimensional drawing having only height and width—neglecting the depth of the ink and paper which in any case is insufficiently thick to represent the actual depth of the body.) Figure 6.28a shows a cube of side 1 unit; the volume here is 1 x 1 x 1 cubic units. Figure 6.28b shows a rectangular block of sides 2, 1 and 1 units. As shown this is equivalent to two unit cubes of figure 6.28a joined end-on; the volume is 2 x 1 x 1 cubic units. Similarly figure 6.28c shows a rectangular body of sides 2, 2 and 1 units, equivalent to 4 cubic units joined as shown and the volume is 2 x 2 x 1 cubic units. In general for a rectangular body of sides a, b and c length units the volume is abc cubic units. For other shaped bodies the volume may be found either by special analysis or by multiplying area of cross-section by length if the area of cross-section is the same throughout the body's length—if the body is of *uniform* cross-section.

Example 6.17
Liquid is flowing through a pipe of uniform circular cross-section having the dimensions shown in figure 6.29 with a velocity of 1.5 m/s.

Determine (a) the volume of liquid moving through the pipe per second;
(b) the volume of material used for making the pipe per metre length of the pipe.

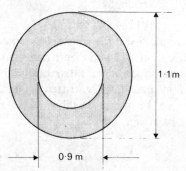

1·1m

Figure 6.29   Example 6.17   0·9 m

(a) The volume of liquid moving through the pipe per second is equal to that of a cylinder of length 1.5 m and having as cross-section a circle of diameter 0.9 m. The length of the cylinder is determined by the liquid velocity, since this is the distance moved per second by any one part of the liquid, and the circular cross-section of the cylinder is the same as the inner circle of the pipe.

volume of any cylinder   = area of cross-section x length

volume of liquid per second $= \dfrac{\pi \times 0.9^2}{4} \times 1.5 \text{ m}^3$

$= 0.954 \text{ m}^3$

(b) The volume of material used in making the pipe is the difference between the volume of a cylinder having the outer circle as cross-section and the volume of a cylinder having the inner circle as cross-section. Thus per metre length of pipe

$$\text{volume of material} = \frac{\pi \times 1.1^2}{4} - \frac{\pi \times 0.9^2}{4}$$

$$= 0.3142 \text{ m}^3$$

Example 6.18

The volume of a piece of copper conductor of uniform circular cross-section of diameter 0.50 mm is 20 cm³. Calculate the length of the wire.

Volume of a cylinder radius r, length l, is given by $\pi r^2 l$. Hence for this case

$$20 = \pi \times \left(\frac{0.05}{2}\right)^2 \times l$$

$$20 = 0.000625\pi l$$

thus

$$l = \frac{20}{0.00625\pi}$$

$$= 10\,182 \text{ cm}$$

Note in this example that if the volume is given in cm³, the radius must be written in cm—since 1 cm = 10 mm then 1 mm = 0.1 cm and 0.5 mm = 0.05 cm. The calculated length is then in cm. Alternatively, the radius may be retained in mm and the volume must then be written in mm³. Since 1 cm = 10 mm then 1 cm³ = 1000 mm³ so the volume would be 20 000 mm³ and the calculated length would then be in mm.

Example 6.19

A rectangular block of material of dimensions 400 mm, 300 mm and 200 mm is melted down and recast into washers 4 mm thick and having an internal diameter of 15 mm and external diameter of 20 mm. Assuming a 5 per cent loss of material occurs in the process calculate the total number of washers obtained.

The volume of the rectangular block = 400 × 300 × 200 mm³. Since a 5 per cent loss occurs, 95 per cent, that is 95/100 of the volume remains.

material volume available for washers $= \dfrac{95 \times 400 \times 300 \times 200}{100}$

$$= 95 \times 24 \times 10^4 \text{ mm}^3$$

volume of washer $=$ surface area $\times$ thickness

$\qquad\qquad = $ (area of outer circle $-$ area of inner circle) $\times$ thickness

$$= \left(\dfrac{\pi \times 20^2}{4} - \dfrac{\pi \times 15^2}{4} \right) \times 4$$

$$= 175\pi \text{ mm}^3$$

therefore

number of washers $= \dfrac{95 \times 24 \times 10^4}{175\pi}$

$$= 41\ 454 \text{ (slide rule calculation)}$$

Exercise 6.4

(1) Calculate the volume of material used in a copper pipe of cylindrical shape and having dimensions as follows: internal diameter 13 cm, external diameter 20 cm, length 120 cm.

(2) A flywheel has a diameter of 0.5 m and a thickness of 5 cm. Through the centre a hole of diameter 2.5 cm is drilled. Determine the volume of material of the flywheel and the surface area of its circumference.

(3) A tank 6 m long, 4.5 m broad and 2 m high is emptied of its contents through a pipe at the rate of 20 m³/min. Determine the time required to empty the tank.

(4) Determine the internal diameter of a cylindrical pipe of length 5 m and having an external diameter of 0.2 m, if the volume of material used in its manufacture is the same as that used for a second cylindrical pipe of internal diameter 0.1 m, external diameter 0.12 m and length 20 m.

(5) Determine the volume of material used in the heat-sink illustrated in figure 6.27.

(6) A 0.1 m thick cast-iron bedplate is rectangular in shape having dimensions 2 m × 1.5 m. Three circular holes of diameters 25 cm, 50 cm and 15 cm are cut through the bedplate. Determine the volume of material used in the bedplate when completed.

(7) Fifty cylindrical ingots of metal are melted down and recast into twenty-five cubes. If the ingots have a length 75 cm and diameter 15 cm determine the length of side of each cube produced. Assume no loss of material in the recasting process.

(8) Determine the mass of material in 10 000 washers, internal diameter 5 cm, external diameter 6 cm, thickness 0.8 cm, if 1 m^3 of the material used has a mass of 20 kg.

(9) Molten metal of mass 100 kg is to be cast into a cylinder. If the metal density is 7000 kg/m^3 calculate the length of the cylinder if its radius is 0.2 m.

(10) A water tank of capacity 1000 l has a trapezoidal cross-section with parallel sides of length 0.9 m and 0.8 m situated 1.2 m apart. Calculate the tank length.

7 Trigonometry

In any right-angled triangle containing the same angles the ratio of any one side to any other always remains the same. Since there are three sides in a triangle there are six possible ratios and each ratio is constant and depends on the angles of the triangle. These ratios are called *functions* of an angle (as in algebra we may say y is a function of x, that is y depends on x). Trigonometry is the study of these functions, their definitions and values, their relationship with one another and the use to which a knowledge of the functions may be put.

FUNCTIONS OF ANGLES

To illustrate further the meaning of the word functions in this case examine figure 7.1 which shows three similar triangles. In each triangle the angle ABC has the same value. Since $\hat{ACB}$ is a right angle and the angles of a triangle must have a sum of $180°$, the angle BAC must also have the same value in all the

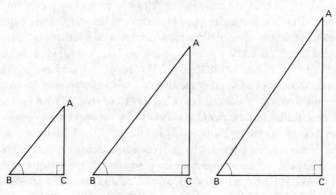

Figure 7.1

similar triangles shown. The value of $\hat{ABC}$, of course, need not be the same as
that of $\hat{ACB}$. In all the triangles shown any ratio of the six possibilities AC/BC,
AC/AB, BC/AB and their reciprocals remains constant.

Consider AC/BC for example. As the triangle is increased in size, that is the
length of the sides is increased, the side AC is increased in proportion to the
side BC so that if AC doubles BC doubles, if AC trebles BC trebles, and so on.
The ratio AC/BC is thus constant provided that $\hat{ABC}$ has the same value in all
the triangles. The ratios given may be said to be functions of $\hat{ABC}$ (or $\hat{BAC}$)
since as the angle is changed the ratios will change accordingly. How they change
will now be examined as each function is considered in detail.

The sine function

The sine function of any angle having a value between 0° and 90° is defined as
the ratio of the length of the side opposite to the angle to the length of the
hypotenuse (the side opposite the right angle) when the angle forms part of a
right-angled triangle.

Thus, in figure 7.1

$$\text{sine } \hat{ABC} = \frac{AC}{AB}$$

$$\text{sine } \hat{BAC} = \frac{BC}{AB}$$

The word sine is often abbreviated to sin (which is however still pronounced
sine). The sine of any angle always has the same value and thus values of sines
may be drawn up in the form of a table. Such tables are usually included in a
book or booklet along with other useful mathematical tables, for example
logarithms, antilogarithms, roots, reciprocals, etc., and the rules for reading are
similar. Obtain a set of tables and examine those for sine functions. The heading
is 'Natural Sines'. The far left column indicates degrees and each column
proceeding to the right across the page indicates fractions of degrees expressed
in minutes or decimally. The five separate columns at the right-hand side of the
page, headed 'mean differences' refer to minutes. Thus sin 30° (sine 30° 0') is
0.5 from the tables. Similarly sin 45° = 0.7071, sin 60° = 0.866 and so on.

To obtain the sine of an angle consisting of a whole number of degrees plus a
number of minutes locate the degrees in the left-hand column then proceed
along the row until the column which is headed by the appropriate number of
minutes is reached. Thus sin 30° 6' = 0.5015, sin 30° 12' = 0.5030, and so on.

If there is not a column headed by the required number of minutes stop at
the column headed by the number nearest to but less than the required number,
then add to the figure given there the figure obtained from the mean-difference
column corresponding to the number of minutes difference between the number

required and that already found in the left-hand columns. Thus for sin 30° 21′ find sin 30° 18′ which is 0.5045 and proceed to the mean-difference column headed by 3 (since 21′ − 18′ = 3) to find 8. Add 8 to the *last* figure of 0.5045 to give 0.5053. Therefore sin 30° 21′ = 0.5053.

Example 7.1

Find the sines of the following angles

(a) 54′   (b) 57′   (c) 8° 24′   (d) 78° 24′   (e) 88° 59′

From tables

    (a) sin 0° 54′ = 0.0157
    (b) sin 0° 57′ = 0.0166 (mean-difference column 3 gives 9)
    (c) sin 8° 24′ = 0.1461
    (d) sin 78° 25′ = 0.9797 (mean-difference column 1 gives 1)
    (e) sin 88° 59′ = 0.9999 (mean-difference column 5 gives 0).

As can be seen the value of the sine function changes from 0 to 1 as the angle is increased from 0° to 90°. Examination of triangle ABC in figure 7.1 would indicate this since as $A\hat{B}C$, for example, is progressively increased the length of side AC and of the hypotenuse AB would become closer and closer together in value, see figure 7.2.

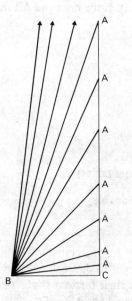

As $A\hat{B}C$ increases

AC/AB approaches unity

BC/AB approaches zero

AC/BC approaches ∞

Figure 7.2

The fact that sines or indeed all functions of angles are constant for a particular angle is most useful in solving practical problems involving triangles where some information is available concerning angles or sides. Before going on to examine further functions consider the next example which shows how knowledge of the sine of an angle can aid problem solution.

Example 7.2

One of the support ropes of a radio antenna mast 20 m high makes an angle of 60° with the horizontal. Determine the length of the rope.

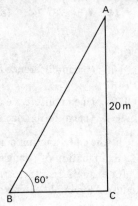

Figure 7.3   Example 7.2

The diagram is shown in figure 7.3. AC is the mast and AB the support rope. Now

$$\sin 60° = \frac{AC}{AB}$$

$$= \frac{20}{AB}$$

Thus

$$AB = \frac{20}{\sin 60°}$$

$$= \frac{20}{0.866} \quad \text{(from tables)}$$

$$= 23.1 \text{ m (slide rule)}$$

The cosine function

The cosine function of any angle having a value between 0° and 90° is defined as the ratio of the length of the side adjacent to the angle (not the hypotenuse) to the length of the hypotenuse when the angle forms part of a right-angled triangle. Thus in figure 7.1 cosine $A\hat{B}C$, abbreviated cos $A\hat{B}C$, is given by

$$\cos \hat{ABC} = \frac{BC}{AB}$$

and

$$\cos \hat{BAC} = \frac{AC}{AB}$$

As with the sine function the cosine of any angle is constant and tables of values are available. These are read in a similar manner to that described above with the important difference that figures in the mean-difference column are *subtracted* from and not added to the figure obtained from the main body of the table.

Thus to find cos 2° 59' locate 2° 54' in the 'Natural Cosines' tables to give 0.9987. Now find the column headed by 5 (the difference in minutes between 2° 54' and 2° 59') and continue along the 2° row to determine the mean difference of 1. Subtract 1 from the *last* figure of 0.9987 to give 0.9986. Thus cos 2° 59' = 0.9986. Similarly cos 45° 40' = 0.6989 (mean difference 8 under column 4 taken from 0.6997 under column 36' along 45° row), and cos 89° 8' = 0.0151 (mean-difference column 2 gives 6).

As shown in the tables the value of the cosine function changes from 1 to 0 as the angle changes from 0° to 90°. This may be seen from figure 7.2 which shows triangle ABC with $\hat{ABC}$ increasing. Clearly the side BC maintains the same length but the hypotenuse is increasing in length as $\hat{ABC}$ increases in size. Thus cosine $\hat{ABC}$, which is determined by dividing BC (constant) by AB (increasing), must become smaller and smaller until it is zero.

The tangent function

The tangent function of any angle having a value between 0° and 90° is defined as the ratio of the length of the side opposite the angle to the length of the side adjacent (not the hypotenuse) when the angle forms part of a right-angled triangle.

Thus in figure 7.1 the tangents of the angles ABC and BAC are given by

$$\tan \hat{ABC} = \frac{AC}{BC}$$

$$\tan \hat{BAC} = \frac{BC}{AC}$$

where tan is the abbreviation of the word tangent.

As with the other functions the tangent of any particular angle is fixed and tables of tangents are available. These are read in the same way as sines, mean difference figures being *added*.

Thus, to find tangent 61° 20′ for example, locate 61° 18′ (the angle nearest to 61° 20′) and read off 1.8265. Now locate the column headed 2 (20′ − 18′) to give a mean difference of 26. Add this to the last two figures of 1.8265 to give 1.8291. Thus tan 61° 20′ = 1.8291.

Examination of the tables shows that the tangent of an angle rises from zero to an infinitely large number (denoted ∞) as the angle is increased from 0° to 90°. This is clear from figure 7.2. In this figure as $A\hat{B}C$ is increased AC is getting larger, BC remains constant so the ratio AC/BC becomes increasingly large.

Exercise 7.1

(1)   Using tables find the following
  (a) sin 19° 21′   (f) (sin 22° 11′) × (cos 42° 31′)
  (b) sin 87° 49′   (g) (sin 42° 3′) ÷ (tan 71° 4′)
  (c) cos 23° 14′   (h) (sin 83° 11′)²
  (d) cos 46° 72′   (i) (cos 32° 4′) ÷ (sin 57° 41′)
  (e) tan 35° 21′   (j) (sin 41° 2′) ÷ (cos 41° 2′)

(2)   Find the value of θ between 0° and 90° which satisfies the following equations
  (a) $\cos \theta$ = 0.4321
  (b) $\tan \theta$ = 0.9871
  (c) $\sin \theta$ = 0.7342
  (d) $\tan \theta$ = 16.83
  (e) $\cos \theta$ = 0.0142

(3)   (a) Find $\cos \theta$ when $\sin \theta$ = 0.3451
       (b) Find $\tan \theta$ when $\cos \theta$ = 0.9872
       (c) Find $\cos \theta$ when $\sin \theta$ = 0.7343
       (d) Find $\sin \theta$ when $\tan \theta$ = 0.4156
       (e) Find $\tan \theta$ when $\sin \theta$ = 0.8910

(4)   Find the sine, cosine and tangent of the following angles (given in radians)
  (a) $\dfrac{\pi}{3}$ (b) $\dfrac{2\pi}{9}$ (c) $\dfrac{\pi}{6}$ (d) $\dfrac{9\pi}{20}$ (e) $\dfrac{2}{\pi}$

(5)   Find the length of the sides marked x in the shapes shown in figure 7.4a–e.

(6)   Find the angles θ in the shapes shown in figure 7.4f–h.

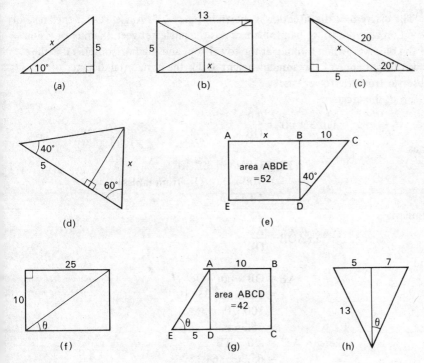

Figure 7.4   Exercise 7.1–questions 5 and 6

Example 7.3

The angle of elevation between an observer and the top of a radio tower is 32° 40′ and between the observer and the top of an antenna situated on the top of the tower is 33° 10′. The observer is standing at a horizontal distance of 100 m from the base of the tower. Calculate (a) the height of the tower and (b) the height of the antenna. Neglect the height of the observer.

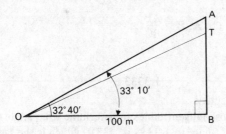

Figure 7.5   Example 7.3

The diagram of the situation is shown in figure 7.5. Angle TOB is the angle of elevation referred to in the problem and is the angle between the line of vision of the observer, when looking at the tower top, and the horizontal. TB is the tower height and AT the antenna height. OB is the horizontal distance of the observer from the tower base.

From the diagram

$$\tan 32° \, 40' = \frac{TB}{OB}$$

thus

$$TB = OB \times \tan 32° \, 40'$$
$$= 100 \times 0.6411 \quad \text{(from tables)}$$
$$= 64.11 \text{ m}$$

Similarly

$$\tan A\hat{O}B = \frac{AB}{OB}$$

and

$$AB = OB \times \tan A\hat{O}B$$
$$= 100 \times \tan 33° \, 10'$$
$$= 100 \times 0.6536$$
$$= 65.36 \text{ m}$$
$$\text{length } AT = AB - TB$$
$$= 65.36 - 64.11$$
$$= 1.25$$

The height of the antenna is thus 1.25 m.

Example 7.4

A town A is situated 100 km due north of town B and a town C is situated 75 km due west of town B. Determine the distance and bearing of town A from town C.

The situation is shown in figure 7.6. The bearing of A from C is Nθ°E where θ is the angle shown. (Bearings were mentioned briefly in chapter 6.)
Now

$$\tan A\hat{C}B = \frac{AB}{BC}$$
$$= \frac{100}{75}$$
$$= 1.3333$$

to four places of decimals.

We now have to use tangent tables to determine what angle has 1.3333 as tangent. The nearest figure to 1.3333 is 1.3319 which is the tangent of 53° 6′. Now 1.3333 − 1.3319 indicates a mean difference of 14 to be added to the last

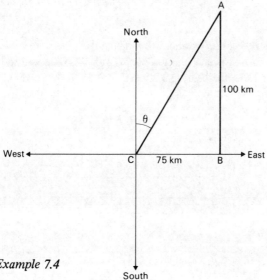

Figure 7.6   Example 7.4

two figures of 1.3319 to give 1.3333. Look in the mean-differences section. We have the column headed 1 which gives a mean difference of 8 and the column headed 2 which gives a mean difference of 16. The latter is closer to 14 than 8. Thus we take the column headed 2 and add 2′ to 53° 6′ to give 53° 8′. (If the required mean difference had been 12 either column could be taken to give approximately the same accuracy.)

Thus $A\hat{C}B = 53° 8′$ and

$$\theta = 90° - A\hat{C}B$$
$$\theta = 90° - 53° 8′$$
$$\theta = 36° 52′$$

So that the bearing of A from C is N 36° 52′ E.

To find AC we may use the sine function or cosine function (of angle ACB) or Pythagoras' theorem since AC is the hypotenuse of triangle ABC.

Using the first of these

$$\sin A\hat{C}B = \frac{AB}{AC}$$

$$AC = \frac{AB}{\sin A\hat{C}B}$$

$$= \frac{100}{\sin 53° 8′}$$

$$= \frac{100}{0.8}$$

$$= 125 \text{ km}$$

Town A is situated 125 km at a bearing N 36° 52′ E from town C.

Example 7.5

An aeroplane is flying due west at 540 km/h and is observed to be at a bearing N 45° E from a radar tower. Ninety seconds later it is observed to be due north of the tower. Determine the bearing of the aircraft from the tower after a further 80 seconds have elapsed.

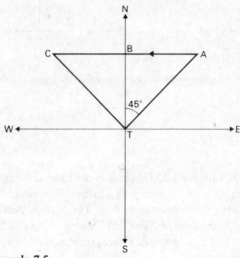

Figure 7.7   Example 7.5

The diagram is shown in figure 7.7. The aeroplane is flying from A to C via B, A being the first point of sighting, B the second and C the situation of the aeroplane after a further 80 seconds. T is the tower so that TA has the bearing N 45° E shown. We wish to find angle BTC. To do this we need to know the length of BC and BT. BC is the distance covered by the aeroplane travelling at 540 km/h in 80 seconds. A speed of 540 km/h is 9 km/min and thus in 80 seconds, that is 80/60 minutes, the distance covered is

$$BC = \frac{80}{60} \times 9$$

that is BC = 12 km.

The length BT (the distance of the aeroplane as it passes due north of the tower) may be found from a knowledge of triangle ABT as follows: in triangle ABT, length AB represents the distance covered by the aeroplane in 90 seconds. Since the aeroplane speed is 9 km/min

$$AB = \frac{90}{60} \times 9$$

$$= 13.5 \text{ km}$$

To find BT use

$$\tan A\hat{T}B = \frac{AB}{BT}$$

$$BT = \frac{AB}{\tan A\hat{T}B}$$

$$= \frac{13.5}{\tan 45°}$$

$$= 13.5 \text{ km}$$

(since tan 45° = 1)

In triangle CBT

$$\tan B\hat{T}C = \frac{BC}{BT}$$

$$= \frac{12}{13.5}$$

$$= 0.8889 \text{ (to four places)}$$

Using tangent tables the nearest to 0.8889 is 0.8878 under 41° 36'. We require a mean difference of 11 to be added to the last two figures of 0.8878 to give 0.8889. Under the column headed 2 we have 10 which is closer than the 16 under the column headed 3. Thus, the angle is 41° 36' + 2', that is 41° 38'. Therefore

bearing of aeroplane from tower = N 41° 38' W

Example 7.6

A ship travelling due east is situated 60 km from a lighthouse at a bearing of S 30° W. Determine the distance from the lighthouse of the ship when it arrives due south of the lighthouse and the bearing of the ship from the lighthouse when it reaches a point 90 km from the lighthouse. The speed of the ship may be assumed constant.

In figure 7.8 the line of travel of the ship is AC via B. L represents the lighthouse. The information given is AL and A$\hat{L}$B. The problem requires us to find length LB and B$\hat{L}$C when LC is 90 km.

In triangle ALB

$$\cos A\hat{L}B = \frac{LB}{AL}$$

and

$$LB = AL \cos A\hat{L}B$$

$$= 60 \cos 30°$$

$$= 60 \times 0.866$$

$$= 52 \text{ km}$$

In triangle LBC

$$\cos \hat{BLC} = \frac{LB}{LC}$$

$$= \frac{52}{90}$$

$$= 0.5778$$

When using cosine tables to find angles from knowledge of the cosine remember that mean differences are subtracted. Accordingly when looking for 0.5778 in this problem look for the number closest to 0.5778 but above it in value so that when the mean difference is subtracted we have 0.5778.
The number 0.5779 lies under 54° 42'. A mean difference of 2 lies under the column headed 1. Thus 1' must be added to 54° 42' to give 54° 43'.
(The minutes are added, the mean differences are subtracted.)

When the ship is due south of the lighthouse it is 52 km from it; when it is again 90 km from the lighthouse the bearing of the ship is S 54° 43' W.

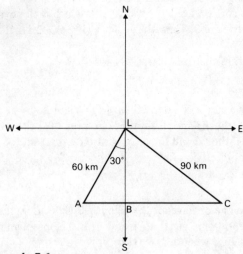

Figure 7.8   Example 7.6

Trigonometric functions of 0°, 30°, 45°, 60° and 90°

Figure 7.9 shows two triangles one with angles 30°, 60° and 90° and the other with angles 45°, 45° and 90°. These angles occur quite frequently in engineering problems and it is useful to commit the values of their sines, cosines and tangents to memory. The lengths of the sides of the triangles necessary to produce the

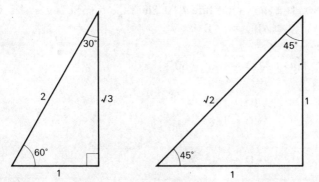

Figure 7.9   Angles of 30°, 60°, 45°

angles are as shown but any triangles similar to these, that is with longer or shorter sides but in the same ratio—as explained in chapter 6—will have the same corresponding angles. Examination of these triangles and insertion of values of functions of angles 0° and 90° as discussed earlier results in the following table

ANGLE	SINE	COSINE	TANGENT
0°	0	1	0
30°	$\frac{1}{2}$	$\sqrt{3}/2$	$1/\sqrt{3}$
45°	$1/\sqrt{2}$	$1/\sqrt{2}$	1
60°	$\sqrt{3}/2$	$\frac{1}{2}$	$\sqrt{3}$
90°	1	0	∞

Example 7.7

An isosceles triangle ABC has sides AB and AC of equal length. D is the midpoint of the side BC. AD = 40 m and angle BAC = 60°. Draw the triangle and calculate the lengths of the sides AC and BC.

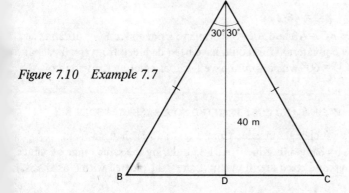

Figure 7.10   Example 7.7

The triangle is shown in figure 7.10. Since the triangle is isosceles

$$A\hat{B}D = A\hat{C}D$$

and since

$$A\hat{B}D + A\hat{C}D = 180° - 60°$$

then

$$2A\hat{B}D = 120°$$
$$A\hat{B}D = 60°$$

and

$$A\hat{C}D = 60°$$

Now

$$\tan A\hat{C}D = \frac{AD}{CD}$$

$$= \frac{40}{CD}$$

since $A\hat{C}D = 60°$ and $\tan 60° = \sqrt{3}$

$$\frac{40}{CD} = \sqrt{3}$$

Thus

$$CD = \frac{40}{\sqrt{3}}$$

$$= 23.1 \text{ m}$$

Now BD = CD and thus BC = 2 CD, therefore BC = 46.2 m.
$\sin A\hat{C}D = AD/AC$ so that

$$AC = \frac{AD}{\sin A\hat{C}D}$$

since $A\hat{C}D = 60°$ and $\sin 60° = \sqrt{3}/2$ and AD = 40 m (given), then

$$AC = \frac{40}{\sqrt{3}} \times 2$$

$$= 46.2 \text{ m}$$

Note that since AC = AB and AC = 46.2 m and from above BC = 46.2 m the triangle is actually equilateral. This could have been deduced from the fact that $B\hat{A}C = A\hat{B}D = A\hat{C}D = 60°$ which would have saved calculating the length of AC.

GRAPHS OF SIN θ AND COS θ PLOTTED TO A BASE OF ANGLE θ

As shown earlier sin θ changes in value from 0 to 1 as θ is changed from 0 to 90°. Also cos θ changes in value from 1 to 0 during the same range of values of θ. Graphs of sin θ and cos θ are shown in figure 7.11 plotted with θ as abscissa,

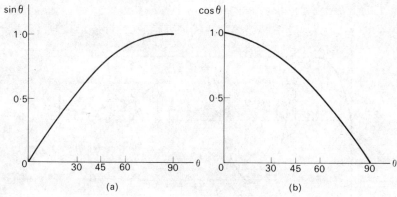

Figure 7.11   (a) Sin θ graph between θ = 0° and 90°
(b) Cos θ graph

the range of values of θ being from 0° to 90°. The range of values of θ may be extended beyond 90° by the following method.

Consider a line OX fixed at O and the point X being movable. Clearly as OX is moved X will trace the circumference of a circle centre O, radius OX–see figure 7.12. Now, let the line drawn from X to meet the reference line shown at right angles be XY where Y is the meeting point. As X is moved to various positions for example X_1, X_2, X_3, etc., Y will also move into positions Y_1, Y_2 and Y_3, the point Y_2 in this case coinciding with the point O.

In the triangle OXY where $X\hat{O}Y$ is shown as θ

$$\sin \theta = \frac{XY}{OX}$$

so XY = OX sin θ and if OX is of constant length the length of XY will be directly proportional to sin θ for all values of θ.

Suppose now a graph of the length of XY is plotted against θ–the graph will have the same shape as that obtained by plotting sin θ against θ. The graph is shown on the left-hand side of figure 7.12. As X moves from X_1 to X_2 to X_3 and so on the length of XY changes from X_1Y_1 to X_2Y_2 to X_3Y_3, these values being shown on the left-hand graph. The corresponding values of θ are shown as $\theta_1, \theta_2, \theta_3$, etc. Note that the peak of maximum value of XY occurs when X lies on the perpendicular through O and is equal to OX_2. The maximum value of the graph is thus X_2Y_2. Note also that beyond the point where this occurs the angle is increasing beyond 90°. Clearly for every value of XY for values of θ between 0 and 90° there is an equal value of XY for corresponding values of θ lying between 90° and 180° and as θ changes from 0° to 180°, the length XY (and thus the value of sin θ) rises to a positive maximum then falls again to zero. If OX is unity the graph is that of sin θ plotted against θ and the maximum value is then 1.

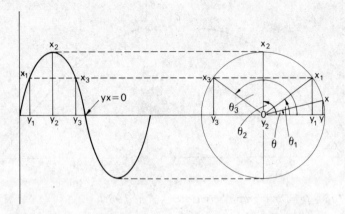

Figure 7.12   Projection of a sine wave

As X moves into the lower half of the circle the graph of the length XY against θ will repeat as shown. XY now lies below the reference axis and is negative in accordance with the sign convention adopted with graphs.

A graph of $\sin \theta$ plotted against θ for values of θ from 0° to 360° is shown in figure 7.13. As θ changes from 0 to 90° the value of $\sin \theta$ rises from 0 to 1, as

Figure 7.13   Graph of sin θ

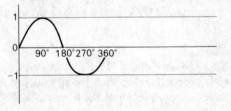

θ changes from 90° to 180° the value of $\sin \theta$ falls from 1 to 0, as θ changes from 180° to 270° the value of $\sin \theta$ falls further from 0 to −1 and finally rises from −1 to 0 as θ changes from 270° to 360°. If a graph of, say, $V \sin \theta$ were plotted against θ, V being constant, the graph shape would be the same but all values would be multiplied by V, the maximum value being V. This graph called a *sine wave* or *sinusoid* is extremely important in engineering because of its frequent occurrence. It will be considered again in some detail in volume two.

If instead of plotting a graph of XY against θ in figure 7.12 we had plotted a graph of OY against θ the shape would have been similar to the shape of the graph of $\cos \theta$ against θ since

$$\cos \theta = \frac{OY}{OX}$$

and
$$OY = OX \cos \theta$$
A graph of $\cos \theta$ against θ is shown in figure 7.14 and as indicated it has a similar appearance to the sine wave but displaced to the left by 90° along the horizontal axis. This will also be further considered in a subsequent volume.

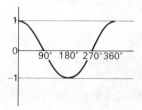

Figure 7.14   Graph of cos θ

The following example uses the word *vector* to describe the rotating line referred to above as OX. A vector quantity is one which has both magnitude and direction—two examples are force and velocity. The word *phasor* may also be used in such problems. A phasor quantity is one which has a magnitude varying with time—two examples are alternating voltage and alternating current.
The terms phasor and vector will be considered in more detail in volume two.
For the moment it is sufficient to be able to understand the generation of a sine or cosine graph by a rotating line, whatever name may be used to refer to it.

Example 7.8

By projection from a rotating vector construct the graph of $y = 4 \sin \theta$ from $\theta = 0°$ to $\theta = 360°$. Use the graph to find the values of θ which satisfy the equations $4 \sin \theta = 1$ and $4 \sin \theta = -1$.
   Construct a circle radius 4, centre O as shown in figure 7.15a. The unit of length used is determined by the size of diagram required. Now continue the horizontal radius OX to the left and construct a vertical y axis as shown.
From the point of intersection of the vertical and horizontal axes mark off a degrees scale from 0° to 360° along the horizontal axis and mark off the y scale from 0 to 4 along the vertical axis. Decide how many points are required to establish the graph (about 8 to 10 are usually sufficient for each half of the graph, a total of about 20). Now construct radius OX_1 at an angle θ_1 with the horizontal as shown. (The value of θ_1 depends on how many points are to be taken altogether, a possible start is 20°.) Draw X_1Y_1 to meet the horizontal axis at Y_1, X_1Y_1 being perpendicular to the horizontal axis. The length of X_1Y_1 is the value of y for $\theta = \theta_1$. This value can now be measured off along a vertical line drawn through the horizontal axis at $\theta = \theta_1$ (shown as $X_1'Y_1'$ in the figure).
X_1' is a point on the graph. This can now be repeated as many times as required to give points X_2', X_3', X_4', etc., projected from X_2, X_3, X_4, etc., as shown.
   Note that once values of θ chosen exceed 180° y becomes negative. On the

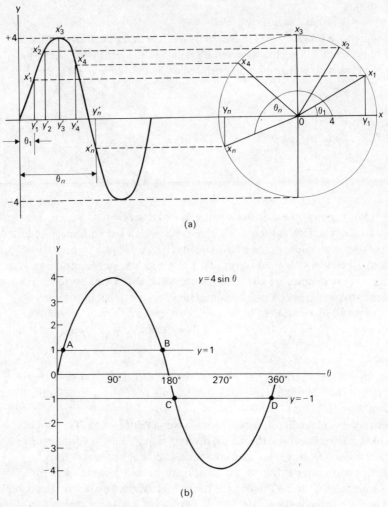

Figure 7.15   Example 7.8

diagram for $\theta = \theta_n$ y has the value equal to length $X_n Y_n$ projected to the graph as $X_n' Y_n'$, X_n' being a point on the graph.

For clarity the graph is redrawn in figure 7.15b. The graph of $y = 1$ is a straight line parallel to the θ axis through $y = 1$. Where this cuts the $y = 4 \sin \theta$ graph gives the values of θ which satisfy the equation $1 = 4 \sin \theta$ since at the points of intersection the values of θ satisfy both $y = 1$ and $y = 4 \sin \theta$ simultaneously.

For $1 = 4 \sin \theta$ the values of θ from the graph are $14° 29'$ and $165° 31'$. Similarly for $-1 = 4 \sin \theta$ the values of θ are $194° 29'$ and $345° 31'$.

Exercise 7.2

(1) A radio mast 25 m high is supported by four cables anchored at ground level at a distance of 10 m away from the base of the mast. Determine the angle that the cable makes with the ground level assuming this to be horizontal.

(2) An observer on board ship sights the top of some cliffs situated 2 km away, the angle of elevation being 12° 4'. Determine the vertical height of the cliff top above sea level.

(3) An isosceles triangle XYZ has sides XY and XZ of equal length. Q is the mid-point of side YZ. If $X\hat{Y}Z = 30°$ and YZ = 2 m calculate the length of side XZ.

(4) An aeroplane flying due east at 600 km/h is at a point situated 12 km from a radar tower at a bearing S 35° W from it. Determine (a) the position of the aircraft relative to the tower after a further 3 minutes have elapsed; (b) the closest the aircraft approaches to the tower during this period.

(5) A triangle ABC has angles $A\hat{B}C = 20°$, $A\hat{C}B = 35°$ and the height of the triangle from point A to the side BC is 10 cm. Calculate the length of side BC.

(6) A town X is situated 50 km due south of town Y. Town Z is situated 40 km due east of town X. Calculate the distance and bearing of town Z from town Y.

(7) The angle of elevation of an observer standing on level ground 500 m from the base of a church tower is 5° 48' to the top of the tower and 6° 12' to the top of a mast on the top of the tower. Calculate the height of the mast, and the height of the church tower. The height of the observer may be taken as 2 m.

(8) A right pyramid is made up of four equilateral triangles standing on a square base of side 15 cm. Calculate the height of the pyramid if the angle between one of the sides and the base is 62°.

(9) A rectangular field of dimensions 100 m x 50 m is divided into two triangular fields by a fence 2 m high and 0.3 m thick. Calculate the volume of the material used in the fence and the angle it makes with each side of the field.

(10) The angle of elevation from a point P to the top of a mast is 7° 22' and from a point Q situated in the same straight line containing P and the foot of the mast and 10 m from P is 8° 25'. Calculate the mast height.

(11) Three towns A, B and C are situated as follows: B is 40 km at a bearing N 30° W from A and C is 30 km at a bearing S 60° W from B. Calculate the distance and bearing of C from A.

(12) A vertically suspended pendulum 50 cm long swings in a 60° arc at the rate of 30 complete oscillations per minute. Calculate the horizontal separation between the limits of travel of the pendulum end.

(13) A triangle ABC in which BĈA is a right angle has a line BD drawn from B to cut AC at D. D lies between A and C. If AB = 25 cm, BÂC = 15°, BD = 10 cm, BD̂C = 22°; calculate AD, DC and BC.

Test Paper 1

(1) Express the numbers 3400 and 0.17 in standard form. Using these results find the value of $3400 \div 0.17$ giving the answer in standard form.

(2) Use logarithms to find the value of
$$\frac{873 \times 14.62 \times 138.7}{18.9 \times 148.5 \times 0.0071}$$
Show the working for a rough check to find the position of the decimal point in the answer.

(3) Use tables to find the following
    (a) $\sin \pi/30$
    (b) $\sin \theta$ when $\cos \theta = 0.2714$
    (c) $\tan \theta$ when $\sin \theta = 0.8761$

(4) Simplify $(8^3 \times 5^4)^3 \div 8^2 \times 5^3$

(5) Solve the simultaneous equations
$$y = 4x + 3$$
$$3y = x - 5$$

(6) An isosceles triangle PQR has sides QP and QR of equal length. S is the mid-point of PR. $\hat{PQR} = 150°$ and QS = 15 cm. Draw the triangle and calculate the length of sides QR and PR.

(7) Using tables find the value of
    (a) $18.7^{1/2}$ (b) $0.187^{1/2}$ (c) $1/18.7$ (d) $1/0.187$

(8) Make r the subject of the following equation

$$V = E - I(r + R)$$

(9) The voltage across a resistor for various currents was as follows

voltage	10	20	30	40	50	60	volts
current	0.1	0.21	0.29	0.41	0.5	0.59	amps

By plotting a graph of current (vertically) against voltage (horizontally) determine the law relating current and voltage. What is the significance of the gradient of this graph?

(10) Calculate the area of a trapezium having parallel sides of length 15 cm and 20 cm, the distance between them being 12 cm.

(11) A pipe of circular cross-section and diameter 0.75 m carries a liquid moving with a uniform velocity of 2 m/s. Determine the rate of flow of the liquid in m^3/s.

(12) Without using tables determine the following
   (a) $8^{2/3}$ (b) $64^{3/2}$ (c) 1.2 radians expressed in degrees

(13) Evaluate the following
   (a) $(7\frac{3}{5} + 2\frac{1}{8}) \div (4\frac{1}{8} - 3\frac{1}{3})$
   (b) $4\frac{1}{6} + 3\frac{1}{3} - 2\frac{1}{5} \times \frac{4}{5}$ of $\frac{7}{8} \div \frac{1}{3}$
   (c) $(2\frac{1}{5} + 3\frac{1}{10})^2$

(14) Determine the value of R_3 in ohms from the equation

$$R_3 = 1/(1/R_1 + 1/R_2)$$

when $R_1 = 2.7$ kΩ and $R_2 = 3.3$ kΩ.

(15) (a) Solve for x the equation $3/(2 + x) = 7/(3 - x)$
   (b) Simplify $(x - 3)(x + 2) \div (x^2 - 4)$

(16) A flagpole 4 m high is supported by four ropes each 7 m long attached to the top of the pole and to the ground. Determine the angle each rope makes with the ground and the distance between the pole base and the point of attachment of the rope to the ground.

(17) A triangle has its sides in the ratio 5 : 12 : 13. If the length of the longest side is 39 cm calculate the length of the remaining sides.

(18) Metal of mass 100 kg is to be cast into a cylinder of radius 20 cm. If the density of the metal is 8000 kg/m^3 calculate the cylinder length. Assume a 2 per cent loss of metal during casting.

(19) Calculate the surface area of a right pyramid, each side being an isosceles triangle of side lengths 10 cm, 10 cm, 5 cm. Include the base area in the total.

(20) By projection from a rotating phasor construct the graph of $y = 5 \sin \theta$ and hence find the values of θ between 0° and 180° which satisfy the equation $\sin \theta = 2/5$.

Test Paper 2

(1) Solve $y = 4x + 3$ and $3y = 2x - 5$

(2) A right-angled triangle has side lengths 10 cm and 24 cm, neither side being the hypotenuse. Determine the length of the remaining side and hence give the sine, cosine and tangent of the angle between the hypotenuse and the side of length 10 cm.

(3) Use standard form to estimate the value of
$$\frac{1964 \times 0.00378}{0.875 \times 756}$$
Using logarithms determine an answer correct to two decimal places and compare the two answers expressing the difference as a percentage of the more accurate answer.

(4) (a) Use tables to find $\sin \theta$ and $\cos \theta$ when $\tan \theta = 2.734$.

(b) Convert $12\pi/13$ radians to degrees without using tables.

(5) Make x the subject of the formula $y = (1 + z/x)^3$

(6) (a) Find the value of $(3\frac{7}{8} - 2\frac{1}{3}) \div (\frac{4}{8} + \frac{3}{5})$

(b) The capacitance C_T of two capacitors in series is given by
$$C_T = 1/(1/C_1 + 1/C_2)$$
where C_T, C_1, C_2 are in farads. If $C_T = 5\ \mu F$ and $C_1 = 10\ \mu F$ find the value of C_2 in farads.

(7) The cross-section of a water tank is a trapezium whose parallel sides are 0.8 m and 0.4 m long. The distance between the parallel sides is 1 m. Calculate (a) the area of the cross-section, (b) the length of the tank if its capacity is 1000 litres.

(8) Factorise $x^3 + xy^2 + 2x^2y$

(9) (a) Find the square root of (i) 0.173; (ii) 1.73; (iii) 17.3; (iv) 173.

(b) Find the reciprocal of (i) 0.124; (ii) 1.24.

(10) By projection from a rotating vector construct the graph of $3y = 6 \sin \theta$ from $\theta = 0°$ to $\theta = 360°$. Use the graph to solve $0.8 = 2 \sin \theta$ for values of θ between 0° and 360°.

(11) Two variable quantities M and N have the following values

M	0.3	0.6	0.9	1.2	1.5
N	4.1	8.1	11.9	16	20.1

Verify that M and N are related by a law of the form $M = kN + c$ and determine the values of k and c.

(12) A triangle has its sides in the ratio 5 : 12 : 13. The length of the shortest side is 12 cm. Calculate the lengths of the remaining sides.

(13) Simplify $(4^3 \times 5^2)^3 \times 5^2 (4^2)^2$

(14) A piece of metal of rectangular cross-section has the dimensions 5m, 10 m, and 12 m. It is melted down and recast into a perfect cylinder of length 5 m. Calculate the area of cross-section of the cylinder assuming no loss of metal occurs during melting and casting.

(15) The angle of elevation from an observer to a tower is 5° 12′ when the observer is standing 100 m from the base of the tower. Calculate the tower height. The height of the observer may be neglected.

(16) Solve for x
$$\frac{5}{3+x} = \frac{7}{2-x}$$

(17) (a) Convert 1.2 radians to degrees without using tables.

(b) The area of a sector of a circle whose angle is 1.2 rad is 0.2 m². What is the radius of the circle?

(18) Evaluate without using tables $[(10^2)^{-3}]^{-1} \times (10^3)^{-2}$

(19) Determine the rotational speed in rev/min of the wheel of a car travelling at 40 km/h if the wheel diameter is 0.47 m.

(20) Two lengths A and B are in the ratio 4 : 3 and lengths B and C are in the ratio 5 : 2. Determine (a) the ratio of $A : C$, (b) lengths A and C when B is 5 m.

Test Paper 3

(1) Simplify $(8^3 \times 16^2)^2 \div 4^3 \times 32$ to a power of 2.

(2) Express the following to (a) three significant figures, (b) two places of decimals

    (i) 137.467   (ii) 1.937   (iii) 1.999   (iv) 14.752   (v) 0.089

(3) Using mathematical tables find the following
    (a) $\sin \theta$ when $\cos \theta = 0.5$
    (b) the reciprocal of 92.7
    (c) the square root of 0.0927

(4) Solve for x

$$\frac{3}{2 + x} = \frac{6}{7 - x}$$

(5) Find the value of the following expressing the answer in standard form. Use logarithms or slide rule.

$$\frac{25.7 \times 971.5 \times 71.2}{36.7 \times 412 \times 0.071}$$

(6) Make x the subject of an equation connecting x, y and z if

$$y^2 = \frac{z - 4}{x^4}$$

(7) Determine the value of

$$(4\tfrac{1}{9} - 7\tfrac{1}{5} + 3\tfrac{1}{9}) \div (\tfrac{7}{8} + \tfrac{6}{7})$$

195

(8) Two circular holes of diameter 0.5 m are cut into a rectangular plate of dimensions 19 m by 7.3 m. Calculate the area remaining and express this as a percentage of the original area of the plate.

(9) A straight-line graph passes through the points $x = 5, y = 2$ and $x = 16$, $y = -5$. Find the gradient of this graph and the intercept on the y axis.

(10) Factorise $a^3 + 2a^2b + ab^2$

(11) Plot the graph of $y = 7 \sin \theta$ and hence find the values of θ between $0°$ and $360°$ for which the equation $3.5 = 7 \sin \theta$ is valid.

(12) An isosceles triangle XYZ having $X\hat{Y}Z = X\hat{Z}Y = 30°$ and side YZ of length 20 cm has a perpendicular dropped from point X to meet YZ in Q. Find the length of sides XY, XZ and XQ.

(13) Determine the total mass of metal in 1000 circular washers, of inside diameter 5 cm, outside diameter 6 cm, thickness 15 mm, if the density of the metal is 5000 kg/m^3.

(14) Solve for q if
$$8q - 3 + 5q + 7 - 6q = 8q + 9 - 4q$$

(15) A triangle has its sides in the ratio $6 : 8 : 10$. If the longest side is 25 mm calculate the lengths of the two remaining sides.

(16) Evaluate $(10^3)^2 \div (10^4)^{-5} \times (10^2)^2$

(17) Find the total surface area of a rectangular box of dimensions 3 m by 0.2 m by 6.2 m.

(18) Town A is situated due north from town B and 100 km from it. Town C is situated due east from town A and is 150 km from B. Calculate the distance between town A and C and the bearing of town C from town B.

(19) (a) Convert decimal 78 to binary.
     (b) Convert binary 101101 to decimal.

(20) Without using tables convert the following angles to degrees
     (a) 1.78π rad   (b) 2.5π rad

Test Paper 4

(1) Simplify $(3 \times 27)^3 \div (9 \times 3^4)^2$ in terms of a power of 3.

(2) Express the following numbers in standard form $37.5, 46.2, 3715, 0.47, 44.3$. Hence give an approximate result of the following

$$\frac{37.5 \times 0.47 \times 44.3}{46.2 \times 3715}$$

(3) A triangle having one angle a right angle has sides of length 24 cm and 26 cm, the latter being the hypotenuse. Determine the length of the remaining side and the value of both remaining angles. Express the angles in radians.

(4) Solve

$$x^2 - 3x + 2x^2 - 4x = 6x^2 - 7x + x^2 + 2x$$

(5) Use logarithms to find the square root of x when

$$x = \frac{17.2 \times 1.03^2 \times 0.094}{1.37^3 \times 1974 \times 0.12}$$

(6) Make C_2 the subject of the equation
$$C_T = 1/(1/C_1 + 1/C_2)$$

(7) Determine the value of
$$(3\tfrac{7}{8} - 4\tfrac{2}{5}) \div (\tfrac{4}{5} + \tfrac{1}{10})$$

(8) A straight-line graph of y plotted against x cuts the y axis at $y = 5$ and the x axis at $x = 6$. Determine the equation of the graph.

(9) Determine (a) the maximum number of discs of radius 5 cm which can be cut from a square of side 1.12 m; (b) the total area of the remaining material.

(10) Factorise $yx^2 - y^3$

(11) Use tables to determine the values of θ between 0° and 360° at which the graphs $y = 4$ and $y = 5 \sin \theta$ intersect.

(12) Find all the angles of an equilateral triangle of side 15 cm.

(13) A cylindrical water-tank of height 10 m is emptied in 4 minutes by an outlet pipe carrying liquid at the rate of 1000 litres/second. Find the diameter of the tank cross-section.

(14) Solve

$$\frac{9}{4y - 6} = \frac{5}{y + 7}$$

(15) Three gear-wheels are coupled such that wheel A drives wheel B which in turn drives wheel C. The ratio of the speed of wheel A to that of wheel B is 4 : 1 and of the speed of wheel B to that of wheel C is 3 : 1. Find the ratio of the speed of wheel A to that of wheel C. If wheel B is turning at 500 rev/min find the corresponding rotational speeds of the other wheels.

(16) Evaluate $(10^{-3})^{-2} \div (10^{-7})^{-1} \times 10^2$

(17) Find the total surface area of a cylinder of height 0.4 m and diameter 25 cm.

(18) The angle of elevation from an observer to the top of a tower is 5° 12'. When he moves 25 m nearer the new angle of elevation is 6° 25'. Determine (a) the height of the tower; (b) the distance of the observer from the tower.

(19) Convert 4.65 (decimal) to binary.

(20) (a) Convert the following angles to degrees without using tables
        (i) $5\pi/12$ rad   (ii) $2\pi/3$ rad
      (b) Convert the following angles to radians using tables if necessary
        (i) 138° 41'   (ii) 235° 45'

Test Paper 5

(1) Express the numbers 4900 and 0.7 in standard form and use these results to determine the value of $4900^{1/2} \div 0.7$. Express the answer in standard form.

(2) Simplify $(125 \times 5)^3 \div 25^2 \times 5$ in terms of 5 raised to a power.

(3) (a) Find the reciprocal of 9.17 and 0.0917.

    (b) Find the square root of 14.42 and 144.2.

    (c) Find $\tan \theta$ when $\sin \theta = 0.8971$.

(4) Solve for x when

$$\frac{10}{12+x} = \frac{3}{x-1}$$

(5) Use tables to find the value of Z, given by the equation

$$Z = \sqrt{(R^2 + \omega^2 L^2)}$$

when

$$R = 14.7 \times 10^3$$
$$\omega = 2\pi \times 10^3$$
$$L = 15.2$$

(6) Determine an equation expressing P in terms of Q, R and S if

$$Q = [\sqrt{(R^2 - S^2)}]P^2$$

(7) Determine the value of

$$(7\tfrac{1}{8} - 8\tfrac{1}{5}) \times (3\tfrac{3}{8} + 4\tfrac{1}{5})$$

199

(8) The resistance of a piece of wire R_t at various temperatures t is as follows

R	100	100.39	100.8	101.18	101.61	102	102.38	Ω
t	0	1	2	3	4	5	6	°C

Determine the equation relating R_t and t.

(9) Find the total surface area of a rectangular box of sides 0.7 m by 0.3 m by 9.15 m.

(10) Factorise $3xy + 9x^2y + 27xy^2$

(11) By projection from a rotating vector construct the graph of $y = 7 \sin \theta$ and hence determine the values of θ between $0°$ and $360°$ for which $14 \sin \theta = 5$.

(12) A parallelogram ABCD has a line constructed from B to meet DC extended at X. If $B\hat{C}X = 30°$, $B\hat{X}C = 90°$ and BX = 10 cm find the length of side BC. If side AB is of length 20 cm find the area of the parallelogram.

(13) An air-conditioning system removes the air from a room of dimensions 3 m by 10 m by 7 m in 2.5 min. Find the rate of flow of the air in litres/second.

(14) Solve for y when
$$y^2 - 3y + 6y^2 - 7y^2 = 19y - 3y + 5y + 48$$

(15) The heights of three men are in the ratio 1.1 : 1.05 : 0.98. Find the height of the shortest man if the tallest man's height is 1.9 m.

(16) Evaluate $(10^3)^2 \times (10^{-3})^2 \div (10^{-2})^3$

(17) The area of a rectangle whose sides are of length a and b can be obtained by using the formula
$$\text{area} = \tfrac{1}{2} [(a + b)^2 - a^2 - b^2]$$
Show that this simplifies to the expression usually used for calculating the area of a rectangle.

(18) An aeroplane flying due east is sighted at a distance of 600 m and bearing N 25° W from an observation tower. Forty-five seconds later it is sighted 750 m from the observation tower. Determine (a) the speed of the aeroplane; (b) the bearing of the aeroplane from the tower at the second sighting.

(19) (a) Convert decimal 37 to binary.
    (b) Convert binary 10111011 to decimal.

(20) Without using tables convert the following angles to degrees
   (a) 3.8π rad   (b) 0.7π rad

Answers to Exercises

CHAPTER 1

Exercise 1.1

(1) 7   (2) 2   (3) 116   (4) 75   (5) 2   (6) 312   (7) 180   (8) 30

Exercise 1.2

(a) $\frac{26}{45}$ (b) $\frac{1}{14}$ (c) $\frac{14}{45}$ (d) $\frac{2}{7}$ (e) $\frac{2}{3}$ (f) $\frac{8}{15}$ (g) $\frac{99}{35}$ (h) $\frac{245}{648}$

Exercise 1.3

(a) $\frac{45}{32}$ (b) $\frac{37}{38}$ (c) $\frac{41}{16}$ (d) $\frac{11}{27}$ (e) $\frac{179}{36}$ (f) $\frac{1}{5}$ (g) $\frac{2101}{54}$ (h) $\frac{31}{19}$
(i) $\frac{428}{189}$ (j) $\frac{57}{4}$

Exercise 1.4

(1) 4^5 (2) 7^3 (3) 9^6 (4) 8^3 (5) 6^3 (6) 7^4 (7) 3^2 (8) $2^5 + 3$
(9) $2 \times 3^2 \times 4$ (10) 1   (11) 2^6 (12) $3^6 + 3^6$ (13) 4^2 (14) 4^{30}
(15) 2

Exercise 1.5

(1) 2^{29} (2) 3^{12} (3) 5^9 (4) 2^{21} (5) 7^{10} (6) $(\frac{5}{6})^8$ (7) $(\frac{2}{3})^{22}$
(8) $(\frac{3}{4})^{16}$ (9) $\frac{3}{5}$ (10) 81   (11) 12   (12) 64

Exercise 1.6

(1) 1   (2) 4^{-7} (3) 3^{13} (4) 2   (5) 1   (6) $(\frac{5}{8})^{1/3}$ (7) $(\frac{4}{7})^{13/3}$
(8) $(\frac{1}{2})^{1/3}$ (9) $3^{8/3}$ (10) $4^{7/6}$

202

Exercise 1.7

(1) 27   (2) 3.75   (3) (a) 0.875   (b) 0.556   (c) 0.909   (d) 0.7
(4) (a) 53.49   (b) 16.9   (c) 7.2   (d) 18.9   (e) 335.55   (f) 8.43
(g) 50.63   (h) 21   (i) 111.91   (j) 7.04   (5) (a) 6.08   (b) 14.85
(c) 3180.96   (d) 178 548.65   (6) (a) 44.44%   (b) 50%   (c) 27.27%
(d) 71.3%   (7) (a) 578 mA   (b) 0.0537 A   (c) 0.000 000 41 V
(d) 275 μV   (e) 5.76 MΩ   (8) greater   (9) (a) 31.8 ; 43.2 ; 733 ; 0.695 ;
1.98   (b) 31.75 ; 43.21 ; 732.8 ; 0.7 ; 1.98   (10) (a) 2400   (b) 2.8   (c) 0.05

CHAPTER 2

Exercise 2.1

(a) 0.6628   (b) 1.6628   (c) 1.5092   (d) 1.5097   (e) 0.5097
(f) 1.8973   (g) 2.8973   (h) 3.8973   (i) 0.4414   (j) 1.4414

Exercise 2.2

(1) 2455.8   (2) 7.309   (3) 35.995   (4) 3.893   (5) 958.5
(6) 0.2482   (7) 0.3452   (8) 2.534   (9) 0.5923   (10) 0.5758
(11) 0.813   (12) 1.4903

Exercise 2.3

(1) 1.9955   (2) 19.955   (3) 0.6310   (4) 0.19955   (5) 0.02662
(6) 0.2662   (7) 2.662   (8) 26.62   (9) 1.6317   (10) 0.05169
(11) 3.3903   (12) 0.10695

Exercise 2.4

(1) 174   (2) 2.61   (3) 2.94   (4) 1.838   (5) 3160   (6) 745
(7) 2 080 000   (8) 480   (9) 19.2   (10) 39.3

CHAPTER 3

Exercise 3.1

(a) $4ax^2 + 4axy$ (b) $25ax + 10a$ (c) $x^2 - y^2$ (d) $7x + 2xy - 7y$
(e) $1 + (1/2y)$ (f) $a^2 + 2ab + b^2$ (g) $a^3c + ab^2c - ab^2c^2 + 3a^2bc$
(h) $\dfrac{x}{4} + \dfrac{y}{4} - \dfrac{6y^2}{4x}$ (i) $x + 2y$ (j) $\dfrac{4}{cd} + \dfrac{3}{ab} - \dfrac{1}{cd} - \dfrac{1}{abd} + \dfrac{1}{ab}$

Exercise 3.2

(a) $\dfrac{y+x}{xy}$ (b) $\dfrac{2+3y+4x}{xy}$ (c) $\dfrac{2a}{a^2-b^2}$ (d) $\dfrac{4bc+3ac-2ab}{abc}$

(e) $\dfrac{6xy+7x^2y+7y^2}{x^2y+xy^2}$ (f) $\dfrac{4x+x^2-12y-2xy-y^2}{x^2-y^2}$ (g) $\dfrac{3a^2+4ab+b^2-4a^2b^2}{ab(a+b)}$

Exercise 3.3

(a) $81x^4+108x^3y+54x^2y^2+18x^2y+12xy^3+12xy^2+2y^3+y^2+y^4$

(b) $\dfrac{1}{2n}-\dfrac{1}{m^3n^3}+\dfrac{1}{2m^6n^5}$ (c) $\dfrac{c^2}{a^7b^6}$ (d) a^4-b^2 (e) mn

(f) $4a^2b^2c^2-8a^2b^2cd+16a^2b^2d^2$ (g) $\dfrac{1}{x^4y}+\dfrac{1}{x^3y^2}+\dfrac{1}{x^2y^3}+\dfrac{1}{xy^4}$

(h) $ab/(a^4+2a^2b^2+b^4)$

CHAPTER 4

Exercise 4.1

(1) $a=\dfrac{bx}{y}$ (2) $x=\dfrac{cy-c}{y}$ (3) $t=\dfrac{V-u}{a}$ (4) $T_1=\dfrac{R_1}{\alpha R_0}-\dfrac{1}{\alpha}$ (5) $b=\dfrac{1}{c+x}$

(6) $i=\sqrt{(P/R)}$ (7) $l=\dfrac{RA}{\rho}$ (8) $c=a^2/b$ (9) $x=\sqrt{(z+y^2)}$

(10) $R_1=R_T R_2/(R_2-R_T)$

Exercise 4.2

(1) $333\ \text{k}\Omega$ (2) $1.5\ \text{k}\Omega$ (3) $333.3\ \text{pF}$ (4) $131.18\ \Omega$ (5) $25.65\ \text{k}\Omega$
(6) $0.030\ \text{s}$ (7) $3.869\ \text{m}$

Exercise 4.3

(1) $\frac{13}{2}$ (2) $\frac{1}{3}$ (3) 33 (4) $\frac{4}{3}$ (5) $-\frac{3}{5}$ (6) -6 (7) $\frac{30}{11}$ (8) $\frac{173}{22}$
(9) $-\frac{17}{28}$ (10) $-\frac{45}{31}$

Exercise 4.4

(1) $x=\frac{17}{3}\,;y=-10$ (2) $a=1\,;y=3$ (3) $a=1\,;b=4$
(4) $x=\frac{53}{112}\,;y=-\frac{11}{112}$ (5) $x=\frac{12}{31}\,;y=\frac{169}{108}$ (6) $a=3\frac{6}{17}\,;b=\frac{18}{17}$
(7) $x=0.13\,;y=-1.29$

Exercise 4.5

(1) 19.23 mm ; 57.69 mm ; 76.92 mm ; 96.15 mm   (2) 75 V   (3) 14 : 135
(4) 6%   (5) 6 : 1   (6) 3.77   (7) 3 : 2

CHAPTER 5

Exercise 5.1

(1) (a) $\frac{3}{5}$ (b) $-\frac{3}{2}$ (c) -1 (d) -1 (e) $\frac{2}{15}$ (f) $\frac{2}{3}$ (2) (a) $-\frac{1}{3}$ (b) $-\frac{4}{3}$
(c) 1   (d) -2 (e) -3 (f) $\frac{2}{3}$ (3) (a) $-\frac{7}{4}$ (b) 4   (c) $\frac{16}{3}$ (d) $\frac{7}{3}$ (e) 0
(f) 0   (4) (a) Intercept on a axis = $\frac{8}{3}$; intercept on b axis = -8 ; gradient $\frac{8}{3}$
(a ordinate), $\frac{3}{8}$ (b ordinate)   (b) Intercept on p axis = 7 ; intercept on q axis
= 7 ; gradient 1 (p or q ordinate   (c) Intercept zero both axes ; gradient $\frac{2}{3}$ (y
ordinate), $\frac{3}{2}$ (x ordinate)   (d) Intercept on n axis = 1 ; intercept on m axis = $\frac{2}{5}$;
gradient $-\frac{2}{5}$ (m ordinate), $-\frac{5}{2}$ (n ordinate)   (e) Intercept on a axis = $-\frac{15}{4}$;
intercept on b axis = 5 ; gradient $\frac{3}{4}$ (a ordinate), $\frac{4}{3}$ (b ordinate)   (f) Intercept
zero both axes ; gradient $-\frac{5}{2}$ (a ordinate), $-\frac{2}{5}$ (b ordinate)

Exercise 5.2

(1) $V = 100I$; gradient represents resistance in ohms   (2) 10 m/s, 50 m
(3) 10.4 m/s ; 0.91 m/s^2 (4) $R = 0.005t + 1$ (5) $E = 49$ V, $k = 20$; 32 V
(6) $N = 10V$ (7) $V = 0.1N$ (8) $I_c = 0.13V_c + 9.32$; 5.175 mA (I_c in mA)

CHAPTER 6

Exercise 6.1

(1) 130 km   (2) 150.013 m   (3) 50.49 m ; 50.64 m   (4) 10°   (5) 5°
(6) Two sides equal   (7) 170°   (8) 4.5 m

Exercise 6.2

(1) 419 cm/s   (2) 272.3 cm, 10.25 rev   (3) 1.59 rev/s   (4) 2.12 rev/s
(5) 30.55 km/h   (6) 30°   (7) 66°   (8) Two 25, 25, 30 and two 25, 25, 40

Exercise 6.3

(1) 1.36 litres   (2) 76 m^2 (3) 683.9 J   (4) 284.8 cm^2 (5) 3.2 m^3
(6) 21.68 m^2 (7) 84 cm^2, 96 cm^2 (8) 29.29 cm^2 (9) 1325 cm^2
neglecting overlap of dividers   (10) 733.1 cm^2

Exercise 6.4

(1) 21 780 cm^3 (2) 9796.8 cm^3, 785.7 cm^2 (3) 2.7 min   (4) 0.335 m
(5) 1938.7 mm^3 (6) 0.2737 m^3 (7) 29.82 cm   (8) 1.382 kg
(9) 0.1136 m   (10) 0.98 m

CHAPTER 7

Exercise 7.1

(1) (a) 0.3313   (b) 0.9993   (c) 0.9189   (d) 0.6794   (e) 0.7093
(f) 0.2785   (g) 0.2297   (h) 0.986   (i) 1.004   (j) 0.8694   (2) (a) 64°24′
(b) 44°38′   (c) 47°14′ or 15′   (d) 86°36′   (e) 89°11′   (3) (a) 0.9386
(b) 0.1616   (c) 0.6788   (d) 0.3838   (e) 1.9626   (4) (a) 0.866 ; 0.5 ;
1.7321   (b) 0.6428 ; 0.766 ; 0.8391   (c) 0.5 ; 0.866 ; 0.5774   (d) 0.9877 ;
0.1564 ; 6.3925   (e) 0.5941 ; 0.8054 ; 0.7387   (5) (a) 28.36   (b) 2.5
(c) 8.47   (d) 4.84   (e) 4.36   (6) (f) 21°48′   (g) 40°   (h) 30°15′

Exercise 7.2

(1) 68°12′   (2) 0.4276 km   (3) 1.1547   (4) (a) S 66°58′ E
(b) 9.83 km   (5) 41.75 cm   (6) Distance = 64.03 km ; bearing S 38°40′ E
(7) Mast 3.5 m, tower 52.8 m   (8) 19.95 cm   (9) 35.496 m^3 ; 26.34′
(10) 10.233 m   (11) 50 km, S 66°52′ E   (12) 50 cm   (13) DC =
9.272 cm ; AD = 14.87 cm ; BC = 6.47 cm

TEST PAPER 1

(1) 3.4×10^3 ; 1.7×10^{-1} ; 2×10^4 (2) 88 836.5 (88 840 using 4 figure logs)
(3) (a) 0.1045   (b) 0.9625   (c) 0.8166   (4) $2^{21} \times 5^9$ (5) $x = -\frac{14}{11}$;
$y = -\frac{23}{11}$ (6) QR = 112.96 ; PR = 111.96   (7) (a) 4.324   (b) 0.4324
(c) 0.05348   (d) 5.3476   (8) $r = \frac{E-V}{I} - R$ (9) Current = 0.01 Voltage ;
Conductance   (10) 210 cm^2 (11) 0.884 m^3/s   (12) (a) 4   (b) 512
(c) 137.45° or 137°27′   (13) (a) 1167/95   (b) 72/25   (c) 2809/100
(14) 1485.2 Ω   (15) (a) $-\frac{1}{2}$ (b) $x - 3/x - 2$ (16) 34°51′ ; 5.744 m
(17) 15 cm ; 36 cm   (18) 9.74 cm   (19) 412.2 cm^2 (20) 23°35′, 156°25′

TEST PAPER 2

(1) $x = -\frac{7}{5}$; $y = -\frac{13}{5}$ (2) 26 cm ; sine 0.9231, cosine 0.3846, tangent 2.4
(3) 0.01 ; percentage depends on estimate   (4) (a) sine 0.9391, cosine 0.3437
(b) 166°9′   (5) $x = z/(y^{1/3} - 1)$ (6) (a) 185/132   (b) 10 μF
(7) (a) 0.6 m^2 (b) 1.67 m   (8) $x(x + y)^2$ (9) (a) (i) 0.4159   (ii) 1.3151

(iii) 4.1593 (iv) 13.1529 (b) (i) 8.0645 (ii) 0.80645 (10) $23°35'$;
$156'25'$ (11) $k = 0.075$; $c = 0$ (12) 28.8 cm ; 31.2 cm (13) $4^5 \times 5^4$
(14) 120 cm^2 (15) 9.1 m (16) $x = -\frac{11}{12}$ (17) (a) $68°44'$
(b) $r = 0.167$ m (18) 10^{12} (19) 451.32 rev/min (20) (a) $\frac{10}{3}$ (b) $\frac{20}{3}$; 2

TEST PAPER 3

(1) 2^{23} (2) (a) (i) 137 (ii) 1.94 (iii) 2 (iv) 14.8 (v) 0.089 (b) (i) 137.47
(ii) 1.94 (iii) 2 (iv) 14.75 (v) 0.09 (3) (a) 0.866 (b) 0.010787
(c) 0.3045 (4) $x = 1$ (5) 1.656×10^3 (6) $x = (\frac{Z-4}{y^2})^{1/4}$ (7) 56/4365
(8) 138.3 m^2 ; 99.7% (9) Gradient is $-\frac{7}{11}$, intercept is -5 (10) $a(a+b)^2$
(11) $30°, 150°$ (12) XY = YZ = 11.55 cm ; XQ = 5.77 cm (13) 64.82 kg
(14) $q = \frac{5}{3}$ (15) 15 mm, 20 mm (16) 10^{19} (17) 40.88 m^2
(18) 111.8 km, N $48°11'$ E (19) (a) 100 110 (b) 45 (20) (a) $320°24'$
($320.4°$) (b) $450°$

TEST PAPER 4

(1) $3°$ (2) 0.005 (3) 10 cm ; $22°42'$; $67°18'$ (4) $x = 0$ or $-\frac{1}{2}$
(5) 0.053066 (6) $C_2 = C_T C_1/(C_1 - C_T)$ (7) $-\frac{7}{12}$ (8) $y = -\frac{5}{6}x + 5$
(9) (a) 638 (b) 0.00124 m^2 (10) $y(x-y)(x+y)$ (11) $53°8', 126°52'$
(12) $60°$ (all angles) (13) 5.527 m (14) $y = \frac{93}{11}$ (15) 12 : 1 ; wheel A
2000 rev/min, wheel C $166\frac{2}{3}$ rev/min (16) 10 (17) 19 642.8 cm^2
(18) (a) 130.8 m (b) 1 162.8 m (19) 100.10101 (20) (a) (i) $75°$
(ii) $120°$ (b) (i) 2.42 rad (ii) 4.116 rad

TEST PAPER 5

(1) 1×10^2 (2) 5^7 (3) (a) 0.109 ; 10.905 (b) 3.797 ; 12.008
(c) 2.0304 (4) $x = \frac{46}{7}$ (5) 9.666×10^4 (6) $P = \sqrt{[Q/\sqrt{(R^2 - S^2)}]}$ or
$P = Q^{1/2}/(R^2 - S^2)^{1/4}$ (7) $-43/303$ (8) $R_t = 100 + 0.4T$ (9) 9.36 m^2
(10) $3xy(1 + 3x + 9y)$ (11) $20°56', 159°4'$ (12) 277.94 cm^2
(13) 400 litres/second (14) $y = -2$ (15) 1.9904 m, 1.8578 m (16) 10^5
(17) ab (18) (a) 17.11 m/s (b) N $43°32'$ E (19) (a) 100101 (b) 187
(20) (a) $684°$ (b) $126°$